SCIENCE FOR EXCELLEN

chemical science

Scottish Schools Science Group

Series Editors:
Nicky Souter, Paul Chambers and Stephen Jeffrey

Authors:
Stephen Jeffrey, John Anderson, Fran Macdonald,
Barry McBride, Paul McCranor and Justine Ryan

The front cover shows a hydrogen–methane flame from the combustion of a gas mixture of 77% hydrogen and 23% methane. This is part of research into the use of hydrogen as a fuel for motor vehicles. Mixing hydrogen with natural gas (mostly methane) reduces the nitrogen and carbon oxide pollutants produced during combustion.

Whilst every effort has been made to check the instructions of practical work in this book, it is still the duty and legal obligation of schools to carry out their own risk assessments.

Orders: please contact Bookpoint Ltd, 130 Milton Park, Abingdon, Oxon OX14 4SB. Telephone: (44) 01235 827720. Fax: (44) 01235 400454. Lines are open 9.00–5.00, Monday to Saturday, with a 24-hour message answering service. Visit our website at www.hoddereducation.co.uk. Hodder Gibson can be contacted direct on: Tel: 0141 848 1609; Fax: 0141 889 6315; email: hoddergibson@hodder.co.uk

First published in 2010 by
Hodder Gibson, an imprint of Hodder Education,
An Hachette UK Company
2a Christie Street
Paisley PA1 1NB

Impression number 5 4 3 2 1
Year 2012 2011 2010

Cover photo NREL/US DEPARTMENT OF ENERGY/SCIENCE PHOTO LIBRARY
Illustrations by Emma Golley at Redmoor Design, Tony Wilkins, and DC Graphic Design Limited
Typeset in Minion 12/15pt by DC Graphic Design Limited, Swanley, Kent
Printed in Italy

A catalogue record for this title is available from the British Library

ISBN: 978 1444 110 777

Contents

Introduction

The first three Science for Excellence titles support learning at the Level Three outcomes of Curriculum for Excellence. This title focuses on the Planet Earth and Materials organisers and draws from the other organisers. It attempts to form a coherent link between the second and third level outcomes. It also makes frequent links to the key concepts identified in Curriculum for Excellence in that the chapters' contents cross into the organisers Forces, Electricity and Waves, Biological Systems and Topical Science.

Where appropriate, the Science for Excellence titles use familiar content and approaches while also embracing the principles of Curriculum for Excellence. The books also attempt to take the topics through to a natural conclusion and to provide, where appropriate, more demanding contexts for pupils.

Modern applications feature prominently throughout each chapter. The book provides many real life examples and applications of the principles which create opportunities for pupils to learn and appreciate the factors which led to the scientific discoveries while also being aware of the implications of scientific advances and their impact on society and the environment. It is hoped that extending the scope of the content beyond the traditional 'chemistry' boundaries will develop a more rounded appreciation of science and society and will lead to greater motivation and a deeper understanding of the issues.

Some of the activities in the book involve experiments. These should only be attempted under the instruction of the Science Teacher and in accordance with the appropriate safety guidelines. Questions and activities are designed to examine and extend the content of the chapters. Skills in literacy and numeracy as well as an awareness of the importance of health and wellbeing will be developed through these exercises – look out for the icons shown at the end of this Introduction. Some chapters allow for numerical and graphical activities while others seek to reinforce the scientific principles contained in the main text. Curriculum for Excellence encourages learners to become active participants and the Active Learning activities in this Science for Excellence series encourage open-ended and pupil investigation activities as well as individual and group project and research work where learners are asked to make informed decisions on scientific advances which may have ethical or societal implications. Tasks are designed around the 'broad features of assessment in science'.

By engaging in the activities and tasks pupils will show features of the skills sought in the 'principles and practice' documentation. Pupils will have the opportunity to demonstrate work that will allow teachers to assess:

- How well do they contribute to investigations and experiments?
- Are they developing the capacity to engage with and complete tasks and assignments?
- To what extent do they recognise the impact the sciences make on their lives, on the lives of others, on the environment and on society?

The principles and practices outlined in Curriculum for Excellence have been adopted throughout Science for Excellence. The series is designed to be used in conjunction with schemes of work which reflect learning and teaching approaches which are most applicable to the sciences. The chapters provide opportunities for scientific enquiry and examples of scientific scenarios where pupils can, for example, improve their scientific thinking or make informed judgements on the basis of scientific principles.

Scientifically Literate Citizens

The use of real data and experimental-type situations will help to develop scientific attitudes. Pupils will be able to look at the data critically and make informed judgements on the basis of what is in front of them. Additionally, they will be critical of broad or bold claims and be able to analyse the science as well as the implications of such claims. Ultimately, the significant challenge for CfE is that it changes pupils' attitudes to science and makes them more able to engage positively in issues that will affect them; that they are able to understand the scientific challenges and issues facing them and respond in a critical and informed manner.

CfE documentation states:

Learning in the sciences will enable me to:

- develop curiosity and understanding of the environment and my place in the living, material and physical world
- demonstrate a secure knowledge and understanding of the big ideas and concepts of the sciences
- develop skills for learning, life and work
- develop the skills of scientific inquiry and investigation using practical techniques
- develop skills in the accurate use of scientific language, formulae and equations
- apply safety measures and take necessary actions to control risk and hazards
- recognise the impact the sciences make on my life, the lives of others, the environment and on society
- recognise the role of creativity and inventiveness in the development of the sciences
- develop an understanding of the Earth's resources and the need for responsible use of them
- express opinions and make decisions on social, moral, ethical, economic and environmental issues based upon sound understanding
- develop as a scientifically-literate citizen with a lifelong interest in the sciences
- establish the foundation for more advanced learning and future careers in the sciences and the technologies.

 **Literacy**

 **Numeracy**

 **Health and wellbeing**

MATERIALS

Chemical Changes

1 Chemical reactions

Level 2 What came before?

SCN 2-19a

I have collaborated in activities which safely demonstrate simple chemical reactions using everyday chemicals. I can show an appreciation of a chemical reaction as being a change in which different materials are made.

Level 3 What is this chapter about?

SCN 3-19a

Through experimentation, I can identify indicators of chemical reactions having occurred. I can describe ways of controlling the rate of reactions and can relate my findings to the world around me.

Chemical reactions

The fireworks display

Imagine you are watching a magnificent fireworks display. Picture the spectacular display of light and imagine the sounds produced as rockets boom across the sky. Can you imagine the smell from the gases produced?

Fireworks have excited people for hundreds of years, yet how often have you stopped to think about how they work? A firework exploding is an example of a chemical reaction. When a chemical reaction happens something new is always made and there is an energy change that shows something has happened. In the case of fireworks, energy is released in the form of heat, light and sound and the gases produced are the new substances.

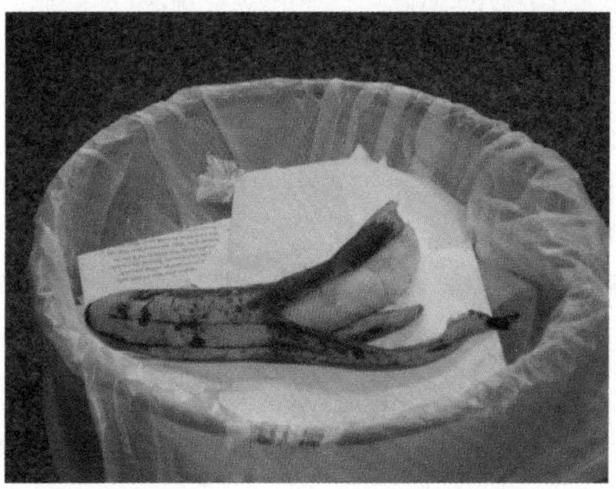

Chemical reactions are happening all the time, but not all reactions are as fast as an exploding firework. Think about the metal chairs in the picture above. Many have rusted. This is an example of a very slow chemical reaction. What about the banana that someone has thrown into the bin? How long before we start to see the signs of a chemical reaction?

The fireworks display

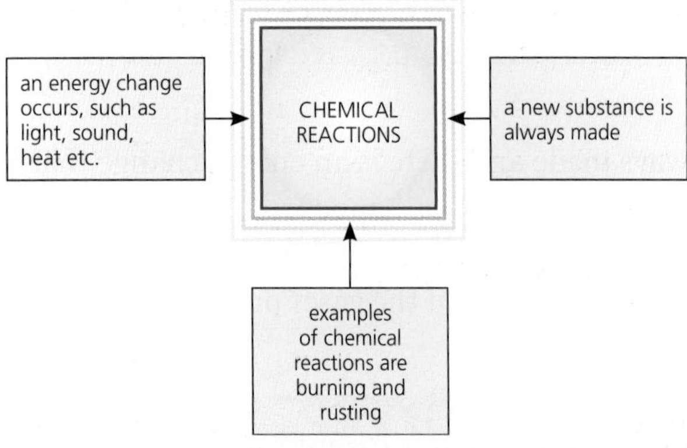

QUESTIONS

1 Think of chemical reactions that happen in the home. Make a list of five everyday chemical reactions and explain how you know that a chemical reaction has taken place.

2 When a cup of water is placed in a freezer, ice starts to form.

a) Is this an example of a chemical reaction?

b) Give a reason for your answer to (a).

3 Think about the rusting chairs and the rotting banana. Suggest how you could speed up or slow down these chemical reactions.

Active Learning

Activities

1 Use flame tests to investigate the metals added to fireworks to produce the different colours.

2 Explore the history of fireworks and make a video presentation of your findings.

3 Debate: How much is spent on fireworks for New Year celebrations in Edinburgh, London and other UK cities? What do you think about this? Should we continue to spend money on fireworks or could the money be spent in better ways? Who would be affected if we stopped spending money on fireworks and displays?

Chemical reactions and energy

Before the Second World War, airships were a popular form of transport between countries. The Hindenburg disaster on Thursday 6 May 1937 signalled the end of airship travel. The Hindenburg was an airship that was travelling from Germany to the USA. As the airship descended to the ground, the hydrogen gas in the airship balloon ignited and caused a massive explosion that ripped through the airship killing 47 people.

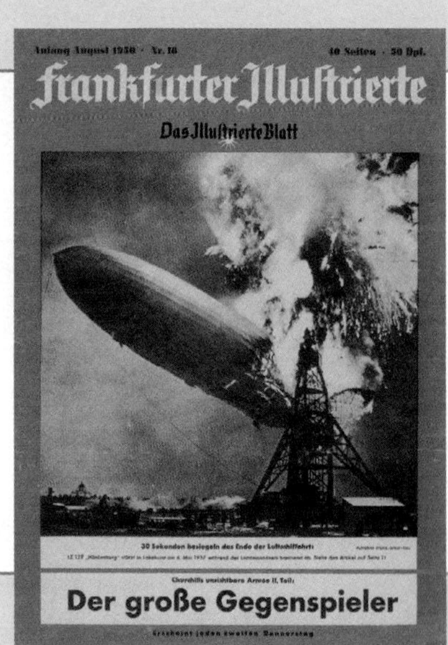

Chemical reactions and energy

The horrific example of the Hindenburg illustrates the massive amounts of energy that can be released in a chemical reaction. Reactions which release heat energy are known as **exothermic** reactions. When hydrogen reacts with oxygen, the new substance made is water. Some energy is required to cause the hydrogen and oxygen to react (this reaction is usually started by a spark or a lit match) but the amount of energy released when water is made is much greater.

Exothermic reactions are used in everyday life. For example, many pharmacies sell heat packs which can be used to help soothe sore muscles and joints. Heat packs usually contain iron filings, salt and carbon. When exposed to the air, the chemicals in the heat pack react and give out heat energy.

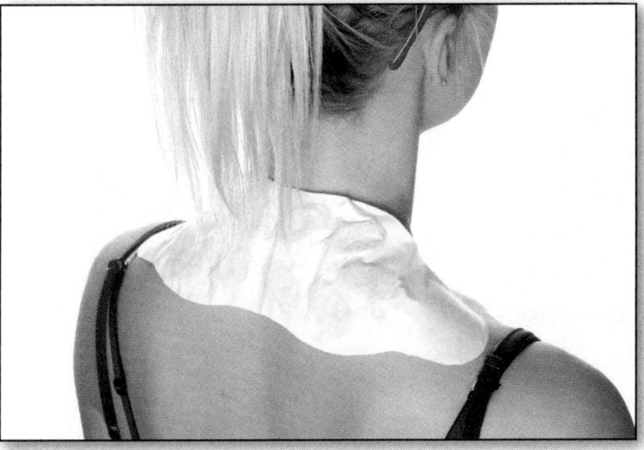

Any reaction which involves burning will be exothermic. Think about the heat released when the wax of a candle burns in air or the heat released when methane gas burns in a Bunsen burner.

Some other chemical reactions take in more energy than they give out. If these reactions take place in a container e.g. a beaker, the beaker becomes very cold as the reaction takes place. These reactions are known as **endothermic** reactions. For example, sherbet contains sugar, citric acid and bicarbonate of soda. When the citric acid and bicarbonate of soda dissolve in your saliva and react with each other, there is a small drop in temperature. This is an endothermic reaction.

Chemical reactions and energy

Cold packs contain chemicals which react endothermically. These can be used to treat muscle sprains.

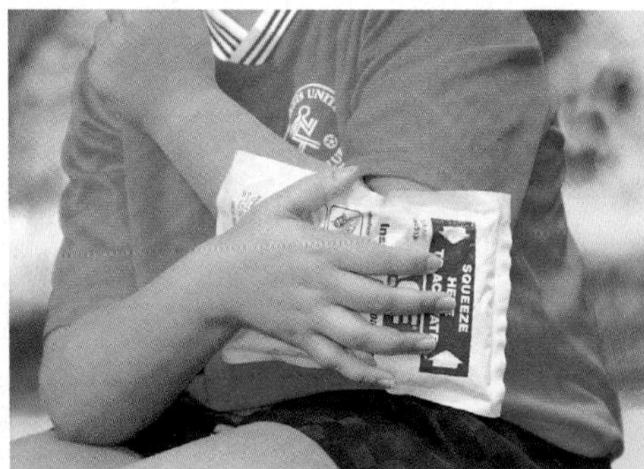

QUESTIONS

1 If you were given one bottle of citric acid solution and one jar of bicarbonate of soda, how could you prove that the reaction of the two chemicals is endothermic?

2 Give two examples of chemical reactions which are exothermic.

3 When a coin is pressed against your lips, the coin heats up and your lips feel much cooler. Explain why this is not an example of an endothermic chemical reaction.

Active Learning

Activities

1 Make a presentation (newspaper/video/PowerPoint) about the Hindenburg disaster.

2 What properties made hydrogen a good choice for an airship? Which gases could be used instead of hydrogen that would be much safer?

3 Make your own heat pack by investigating the best combination of chemicals (iron fillings, active carbon and salt) to give out the most heat. Create an advert for your heat pack.

4 Make your own sherbet and investigate the best combination of chemicals (citric acid and bicarbonate of soda) to give the lowest temperature.

5 Investigate a series of reactions to find out which ones are exothermic and which ones are endothermic.

Speed of reactions

Scientists have developed ways of controlling chemical reactions. For example, the speed of rusting can be slowed down by painting over the exposed metal. Even the chemical reactions that make food change can be controlled. Simply putting food in the fridge slows reactions as the temperature is much lower.

Speed of reactions

Sometimes we are interested in speeding up reactions. Think of the chef serving hot filled rolls and drinks to the hungry spectators at the fireworks display. If he wants to cook an onion to add flavour to his secret burger recipe, he will cut it up into smaller pieces to ensure that it cooks much faster. He will also increase the temperature of the oven to make sure his bread is ready much faster. Making particles smaller and increasing the temperature are just two ways of speeding up a chemical reaction.

Fireworks involve very fast burning. Most things burn in air that contains approximately 21% oxygen gas. Fireworks contain compounds such as nitrates and chlorates which react to create oxygen so that the chemicals burn in a much higher concentration of oxygen. This causes a very fast reaction which we see as an explosion!

The previous examples illustrate three factors which can affect the speed of chemical reactions. The factors are: temperature, concentration and particle size.

The effects of these factors can be observed by carrying out experiments with magnesium and hydrochloric acid. When these chemicals react, hydrogen gas is produced. You can measure the speed of the reaction by timing how long it takes the reaction to produce a fixed volume of gas e.g. 10 cm^3.

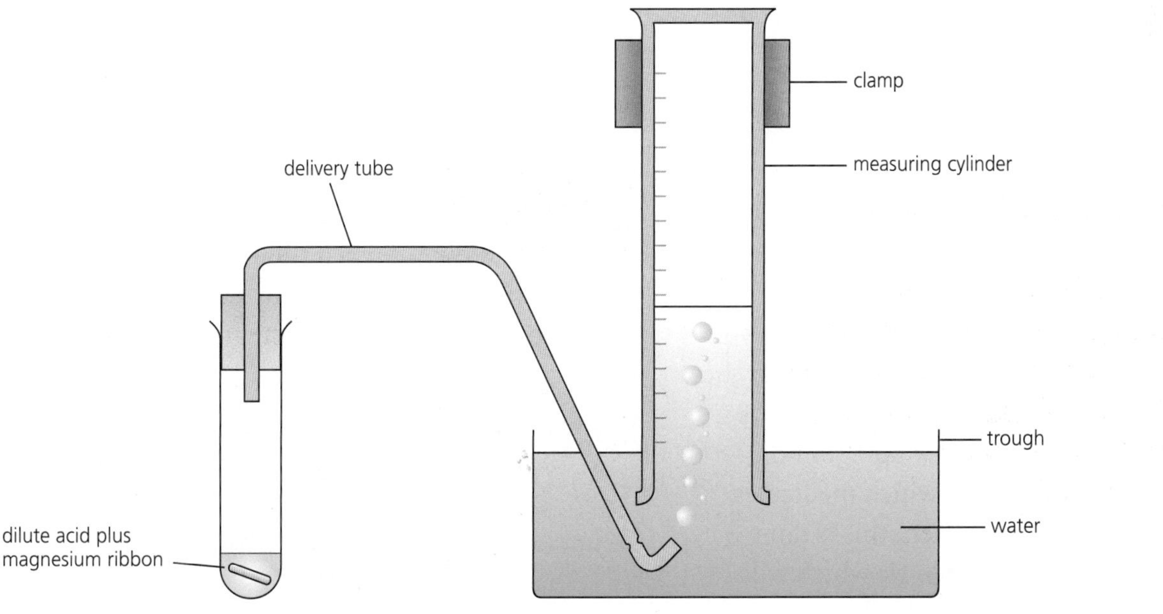

Speed of reactions

Changing the particle size

Magnesium powder and magnesium ribbon.

The time taken for the reaction between magnesium and acid to produce 10 cm^3 of gas was compared with the time it took magnesium powder to produce the same volume of gas.

Experiment	Time (s)
Magnesium ribbon + acid	48
Magnesium powder + acid	22

Using the magnesium powder results in a much faster reaction because smaller particles react much faster than larger particles.

Changing the concentration

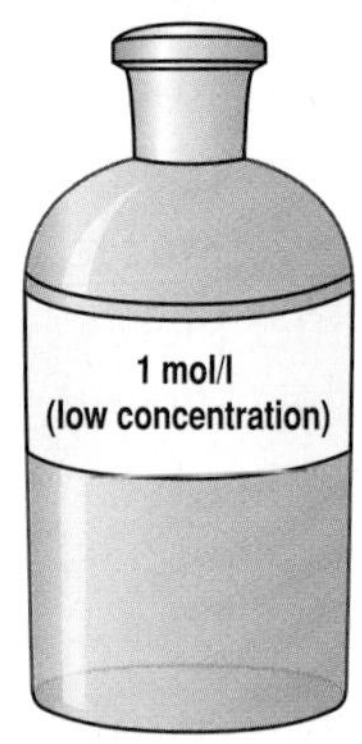

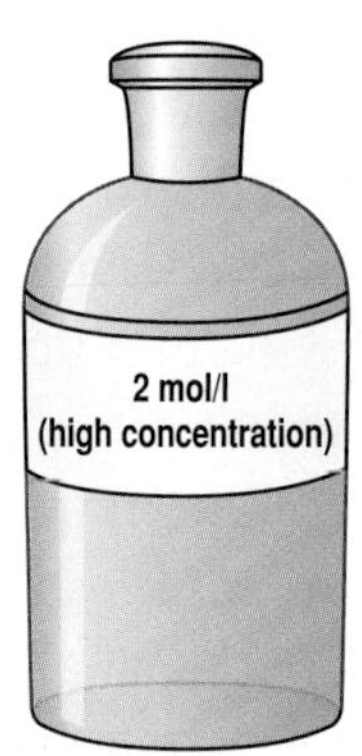

Repeating the previous experiment using magnesium ribbon and different concentrations of hydrochloric acid allows us to observe the effect on the speed of the reaction when the concentration of one of the reactants is changed.

Experiment	Time (s)
Magnesium ribbon + 1 mol/l acid	50s
Magnesium ribbon + 2 mol/l acid	30s

Using a higher concentration results in a much faster reaction.

Chemical reactions and medicine

One of the fascinating areas of science where changing the speed of reaction can have life-changing consequences is in medical research. Some medicines are not very effective in the human body because they do not reach their target or they get used up by the body far too quickly e.g. some painkillers treat pain effectively, but the pain relief only lasts for a short time. Scientists have been working to create new compounds which slow down the speed at which medicines are used by the body. Quite often, this is done by coating the medicine in a plastic which will react very slowly in the body and help to release the medicine over a longer period of time. Other developments include creating compounds which will only release the medicine when it has reached the correct part of the body. For example, some medicines break up in the acid environment of the stomach and do not reach their destination. This can be solved by coating the medicine in special compounds that will not react with the acid in the stomach.

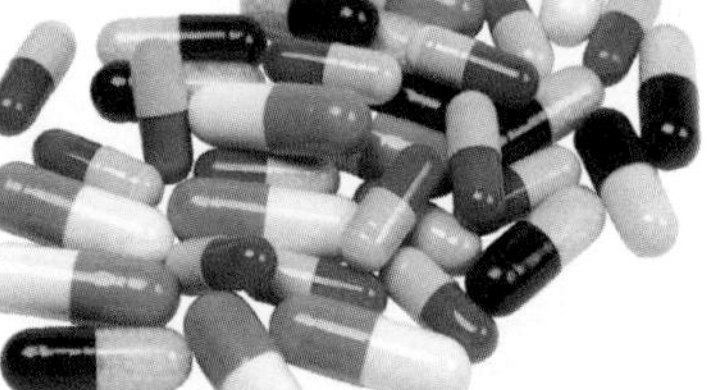

Chemical reactions and medicine

QUESTIONS

1 From the experiment comparing the particle size of magnesium, list three variables that would have to be kept constant to ensure the test was fair.

2 Suggest how you could carry out the magnesium and acid experiment to investigate the effect of temperature. State the result you would expect.

3 Give two examples of chemical reactions where changing the temperature, concentration or particle size affects the speed of reaction.

4 Apart from rusting, can you think of any other reactions which we would like to slow down?

5 A lump of iron will react with acid to produce hydrogen gas. Make a list of all the things you could do to make this reaction go (a) faster and (b) slower.

6 Explain the following: the gas in a Bunsen burner will burn much better when the air hole is open than when it is closed.

Active Learning

Activities

1 Investigate the effect of particle size, concentration and temperature by reacting magnesium with hydrochloric acid and timing how long it takes to produce 10 cm^3 of gas.

2 Investigate another method for measuring the speed of the magnesium/acid reaction e.g. use a balance to measure the loss in mass.

3 Find out about three medicines which have slow release (or timed release) mechanisms. Find out what they are used to treat and why they must be slow release.

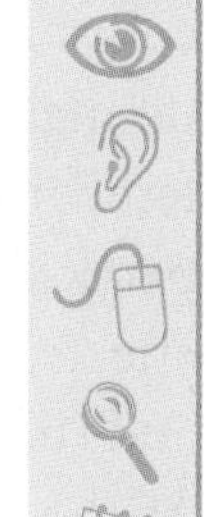

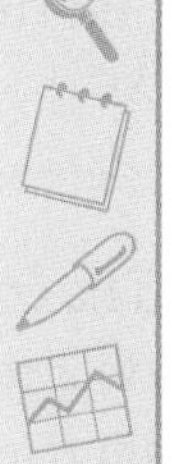

It's all about collisions!

You know that changing the temperature, concentration and particle size can affect the speed of a reaction. Why do these changes cause the speed to change?

For any chemical reaction to happen, the reacting particles must collide with each other. If these collisions have enough energy, the particles will join to make a new product and a chemical reaction will take place.

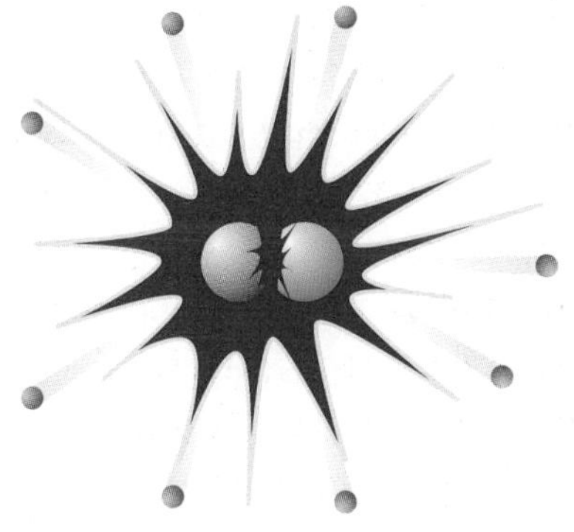

It's all about collisions!

Anything which increases the chance of collisions and anything which increases the energy of the collisions will result in more chemical reactions taking place. Think about increasing the temperature. As the temperature is increased, the particles move about much faster. This has two effects: (i) the particles are more likely to collide and (ii) they collide with much greater energy. As the temperature is increased, there is a rapid increase in reaction speed.

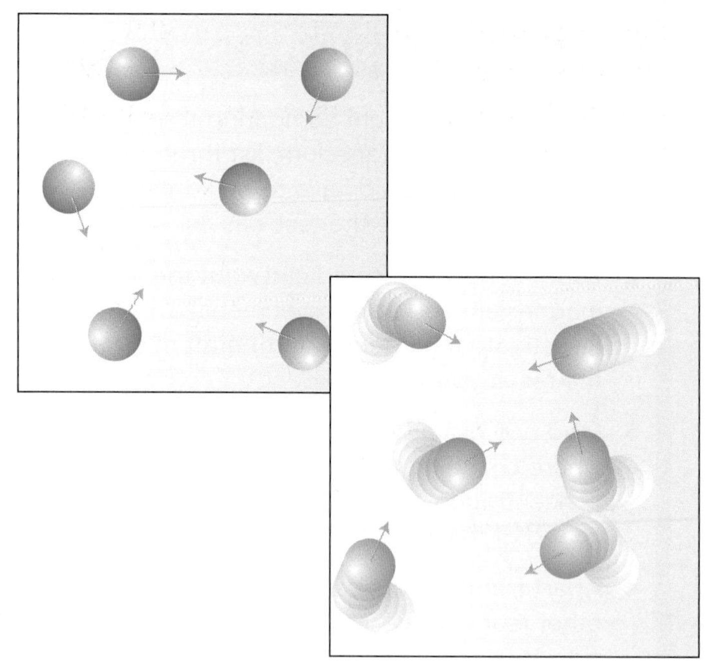

The colliding particles can be compared to cars on a road. Increasing the temperature is like increasing the speed of the cars. You can imagine that there would be many more collisions on our roads if the average speed of a car increased from 30 mph to 300 mph!

Concentration

Increasing the concentration simply means that there are more particles in the same space. This means that there is more chance of a collision. Compare this to cars on the road. Imagine a country road with five cars travelling along at 30 mph. Now imagine the same country road with 500 cars travelling along at 30 mph. There's a much greater chance of a collision.

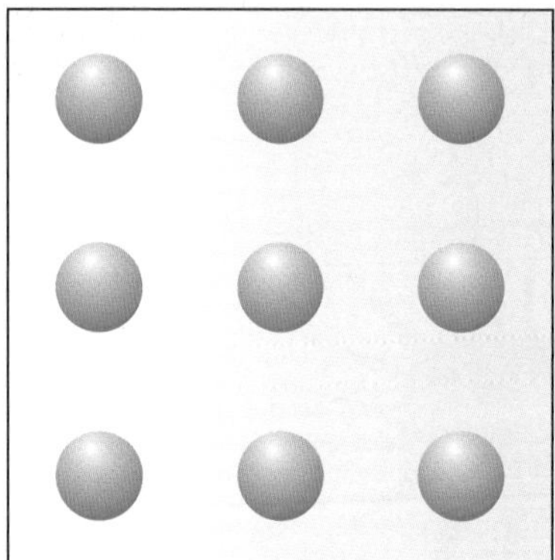

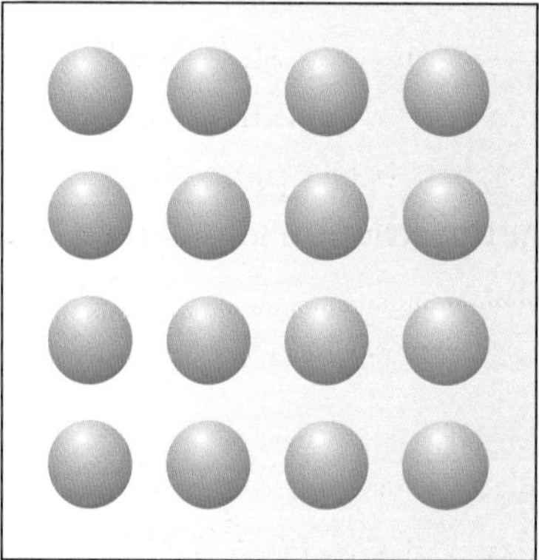

Particle size

When a solid reacts, the only particles which can collide are those on the surface.

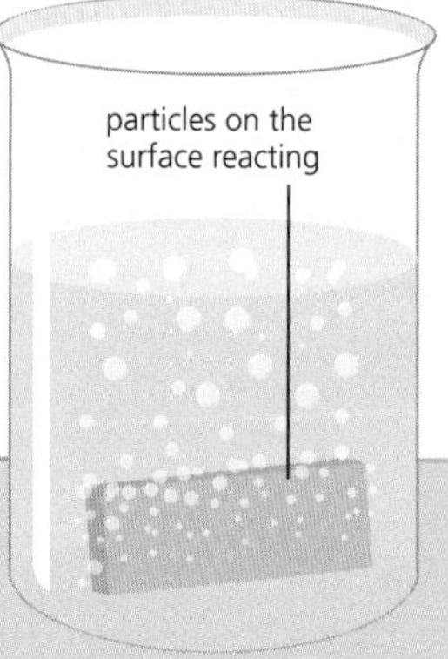

Breaking a solid lump into smaller particles increases the surface area. There are now many more particles exposed so there is more chance of a collision.

QUESTIONS

1 When calcium carbonate reacts with an acid, carbon dioxide gas is produced.

(a) Suggest three ways that the speed of this reaction could be increased.

(b) For one of the methods you mentioned for increasing the speed of reaction, explain why the reaction speed increases in terms of collisions.

2 Draw a cartoon to explain how the **collision theory** helps us to explain how the speed of a reaction can be increased.

Catalysts

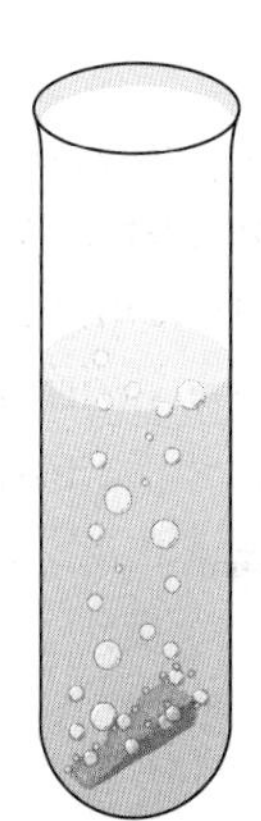

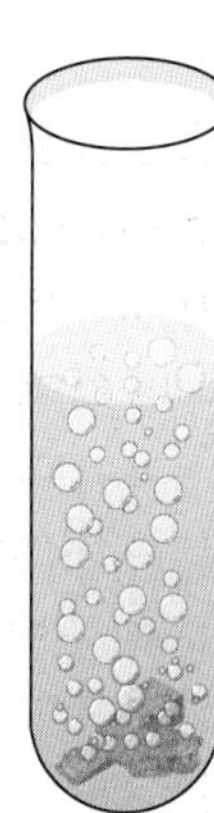

In some chemical reactions, it is too difficult to alter the temperature, concentration or particle size to produce the desired change in speed of the reaction. Fortunately, substances called **catalysts** can be added to chemical reactions which cause the reaction speed to increase. For example, when zinc is added to sulphuric acid, bubbles of hydrogen gas are produced. If the experiment is repeated with some copper added, the reaction between the zinc and sulphuric acid is much faster.

We say that the copper has acted as a catalyst as it has caused the speed of the reaction to increase. Another point to note about a catalyst is that it is not used up in the chemical reaction. In the case of the zinc acid reaction, there is no zinc left at the end of the reaction, but the copper remains. In fact, the copper metal can be removed from the reaction and can be used again in another reaction.

Catalysts in everyday life

Catalysts are very important to industrial chemists as many of the chemical reactions they use require a catalyst. For example, making plastics, fertilisers, explosives and medicines all use catalysts. Most of these catalysts are transition metals, such as copper. You will learn about transition metals in Chapter 3.

One of the great advantages of finding a catalyst which speeds up a reaction is that it can save energy as the catalyst can allow a chemical reaction to take place at a much lower temperature.

Catalysts

The catalytic converter

Pollution from car exhausts has always been a concern because of the danger it poses to our health.

Carl Keith was a research chemist who invented, with his colleague John J. Mooney, the catalytic converter. The **catalytic converter** contains a transition metal, such as platinum, palladium or rhodium, and is used to speed up the change of harmful gases from a car exhaust into less harmful ones (see Chapter 9 for more information).

Some scientists have estimated that hundreds of thousands of lives have been saved by the use of the catalytic convertor, such was the damage caused by the toxic emissions from car exhausts before its invention.

Hydrogen peroxide

Hydrogen peroxide has the chemical formula H_2O_2 and is regarded by many chemists as a 'wonder chemical' because it has so many uses. For example, it is used to bleach paper, as a hair dye and has been found to be responsible for many chemical reactions in the human body, many of which are still being researched.

Hydrogen peroxide is an unstable chemical which slowly breaks down into water and oxygen, but the speed of this reaction can be increased by adding a catalyst.

Hydrogen peroxide → Water + Oxygen

For example, if manganese oxide is added to a test tube of hydrogen peroxide, oxygen is generated and steam can be seen coming out of the test tube.

This reaction happens when hydrogen peroxide is used to clean wounds. When it is applied to a cut, a catalyst in blood known as catalase causes the hydrogen peroxide to break down into water and oxygen. It is believed that the high concentration

Hydrogen peroxide

of oxygen helps to destroy bacteria that could infect the cut.

Hydrogen peroxide has recently gained notoriety as it was one of the chemicals that terrorists tried to smuggle onto an aeroplane to make an explosive. Consequently, airports now limit the volume, and type, of liquids which people can carry on planes.

An unwanted reaction

Sometimes catalysts cause an unwanted reaction. For example, copper, iron and nickel are often present in food either from their presence in the soil, where the food was grown, or from the metals used in the factories, or from the metal containers used to store the foods. These metals cause the foods to react much faster with oxygen and this causes them to spoil much faster. To prevent this, many foods have a chemical called EDTA added to them (for example, look at the ingredients of a jar of mayonnaise). EDTA is a chemical which is able to bond to metals. This prevents them from acting as catalysts for the reactions which spoil the food.

QUESTIONS

A pupil added 1 g of copper metal catalyst to a reaction containing zinc and acid.

Describe how the pupil could recover the catalyst so that it could be re-used.

Active Learning

Activities

1. Research the air pollution in your town/city. Find out when the levels of carbon monoxide and nitrogen oxides were at their highest over the past week/month/year.
2. Prepare a video clip on the discovery of the catalytic convertor. Explain how it works and explain why it was such an important discovery.
3. Investigate the zinc/acid reaction with/without a catalyst.
4. Investigate the breakdown of hydrogen peroxide with/without a catalyst.

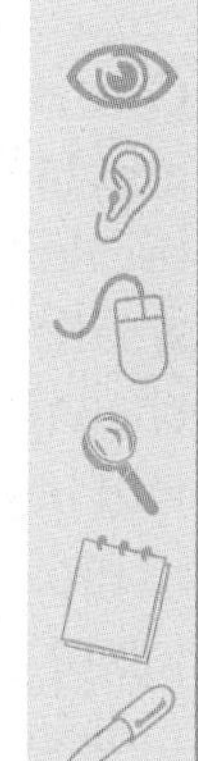

Active Learning

5 Look at the ingredient labels of some common foods. List the foods which contain EDTA. Try to find out why EDTA is added. Which metals are the manufacturers trying to stop so that the food does not spoil too quickly? Contact the manufacturer.

6 Using chemicals supplied by your teacher, can you come up with a simple experiment that will allow you to tell if a liquid is hydrogen peroxide? Why might this be useful?

Enzymes

The human body is an amazing chemical factory where thousands of chemical reactions take place every second! The simple act of digesting a piece of food to provide us with energy and to help our bodies grow and repair involves many chemical reactions, yet our human body is able to complete the process in a few hours. Reactions in living things are able to proceed at such speed because they are helped by catalysts known as **enzymes**. There are thousands of enzymes and they are responsible for keeping living things alive.

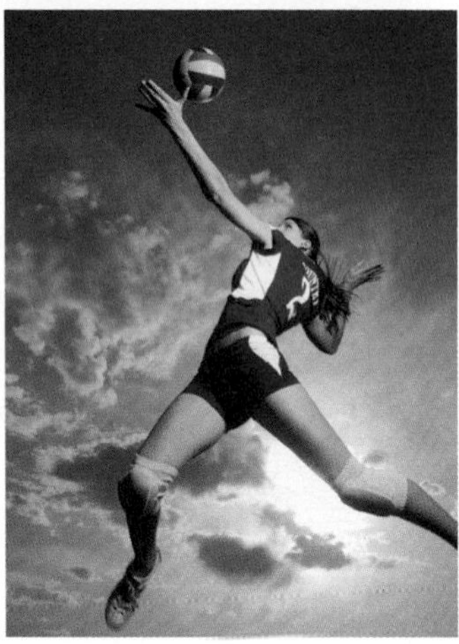

One enzyme present in your saliva is known as **amylase**. As you chew food, amylase speeds up the breakdown of large starch molecules into much smaller sugar molecules known as maltose. (Try chewing a piece of bread for a few minutes and you will be able to taste the sugar.) The breakdown of maltose into an even smaller sugar, glucose, is the job of another enzyme called **maltase**. Small sugar molecules can pass into the bloodstream where they can be used by the body for energy.

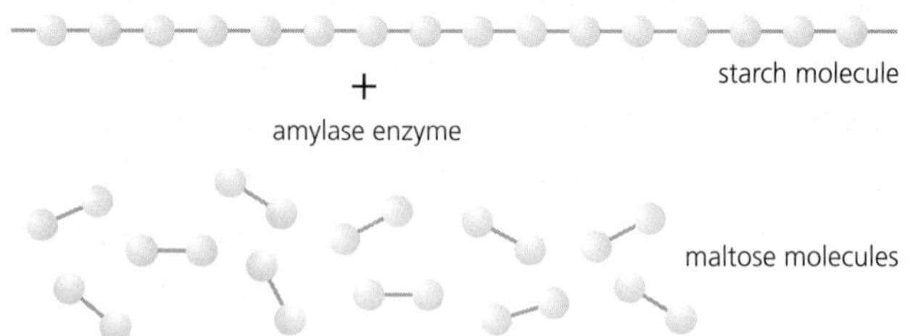

It is not just in human beings that enzymes play a crucial role in keeping us alive; plants rely on enzymes to help them function. The Venus Flytrap is a plant that can trap insects and digest them! Once an insect is caught in its trap, digestive enzymes are released. This drowns the captured prey and allows the plant to absorb the nutrients from the insect.

There are many uses of enzymes in industry. For example, yeast contains the enzyme **zymase** which speeds up the conversion of sugar into alcohol. Many washing powders also contain enzymes which help break down stains so that clothes can be washed at a much lower temperature. These

Enzymes

are known as 'biological' washing powders as they contain enzymes. A common type of enzyme used in washing powders is a **protease** as these help to break down proteins, which are found in many food and blood stains.

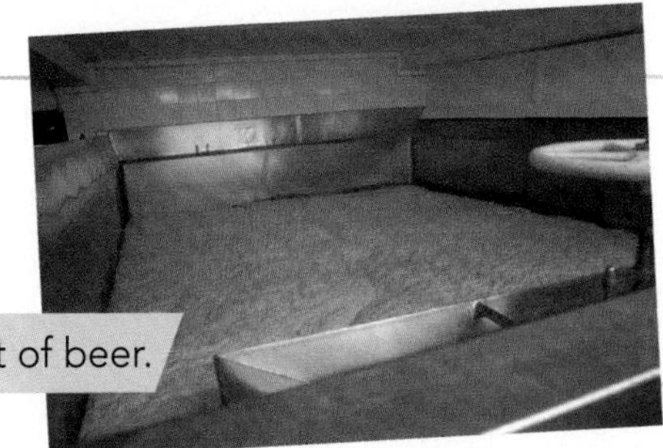

Yeast brewing on a vat of beer.

How do catalysts and enzymes work?

All chemical reactions involve molecules colliding with sufficient energy. Catalysts help this process by providing a surface for reactant molecules to stick to so that they can collide more easily. As the molecules are stuck onto the surface of the catalyst, less energy is required for a reaction to take place compared with a reaction where the reactants are moving about.

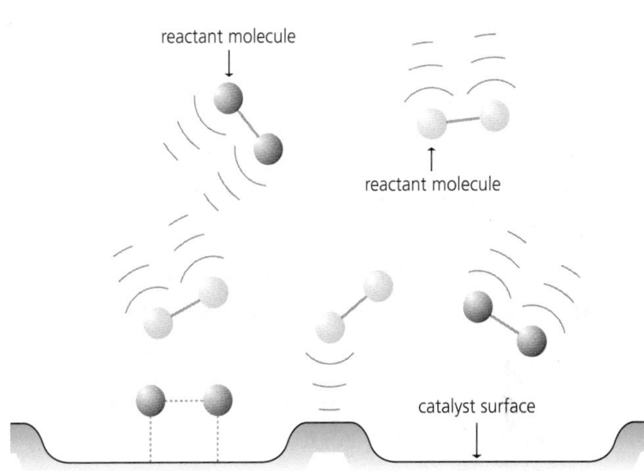

Enzymes also provide a surface for reactants to meet, but the shape of an enzyme is very specific so that it only attracts certain reactants. For example, the enzyme amylase has a shape which is specific for starch and can easily break down starch, but it cannot break down fat molecules as fats have a very different shape.

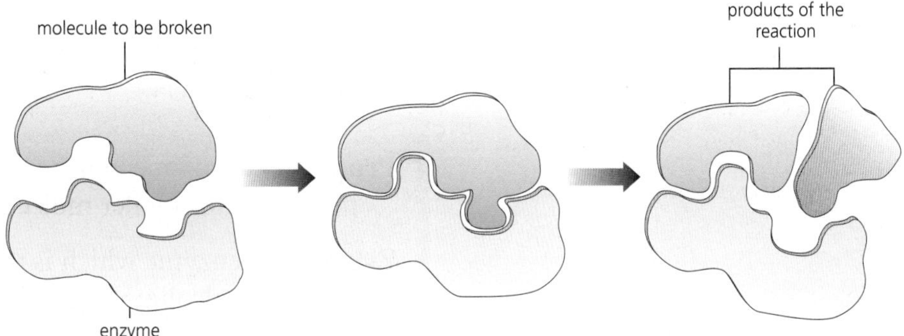

QUESTIONS

1. Find out the names of four enzymes found in the human body and state what they do.
2. Many enzymes stop working when they are exposed to high temperatures. What effect do you think the temperature has on the enzyme to cause it to stop working?

Active Learning

Activities

1 Investigate the fermentation of sugar from different fruits.

2 Investigate the enzymes present in different washing powders and conduct washing experiments with biological and non-biological washing powders.

3 Make a video presentation on the uses of enzymes in everyday life.

4 Try making four different jellies containing the following fruits: a) pineapple, b) satsumas, c) apple and d) kiwi. Try to explain your observations.

5 Add a piece of liver or potato to hydrogen peroxide and explain your observations.

GLOSSARY

Amylase an enzyme found in saliva which helps food break down

Catalyst a substance which speeds up chemical reactions

Catalytic converter the catalyst found in a car exhaust which changes harmful exhaust gases into less harmful gases

Collision theory a theory which is used to explain how changing the concentration, temperature, particle size and using a catalyst can affect the speed of a reaction. It says that particles must a) collide and b) have enough energy before a chemical reaction occurs

Enzyme a catalyst found in living things

Exothermic a chemical reaction which releases heat energy, causing the temperature of the reaction mixture to increase

Endothermic a chemical reaction which takes in heat energy, causing the temperature of the reaction mixture to fall

Maltase an enzyme which breaks down the sugar maltose

Protease an enzyme which breaks down proteins into smaller molecules

Zymase an enzyme which is used to change sugar into alcohol

MATERIALS

Chemical Changes

2

Making and breaking compounds

Level 2 What came before?

SCN 2-15a

By contributing to investigations into familiar substances to produce other substances, I can describe how their characteristics have changed.

Level 3 What is this chapter about?

SCN 3-15b

Having contributed to a variety of practical activities to make and break down compounds, I can describe examples of how the properties of compounds are different from their constituent elements.

Making and breaking compounds

Elements and compounds

What is an **element**? An element is a simple substance which cannot be broken down into anything simpler. The reason for an element's simplicity is that it is made up of only one type of atom. For example, hydrogen is an element because its molecules are made up of only hydrogen atoms. Oxygen is an element because its molecules are made up of only oxygen atoms. Water is not an element because its molecules contain both hydrogen and oxygen atoms.

What is a compound?

Water is known as a **compound** as it is made of hydrogen atoms chemically joined to oxygen atoms. When atoms join together, the properties of the compound formed are completely different from the properties of the elements which formed it. Think about water: it is a colourless liquid which keeps us alive and can be used to put out a burning fire. Oxygen and hydrogen are gases and would not extinguish a fire! Oxygen is the gas used when things burn and so would make a fire burn even brighter! Hydrogen gas is explosive.

Most substances in nature exist as compounds. When did you last go to the seaside? Sand is a compound of silicon joined to oxygen; seawater contains salt, which is a compound of sodium joined to chlorine. A little research will show that these compounds are very different from the elements they are made from.

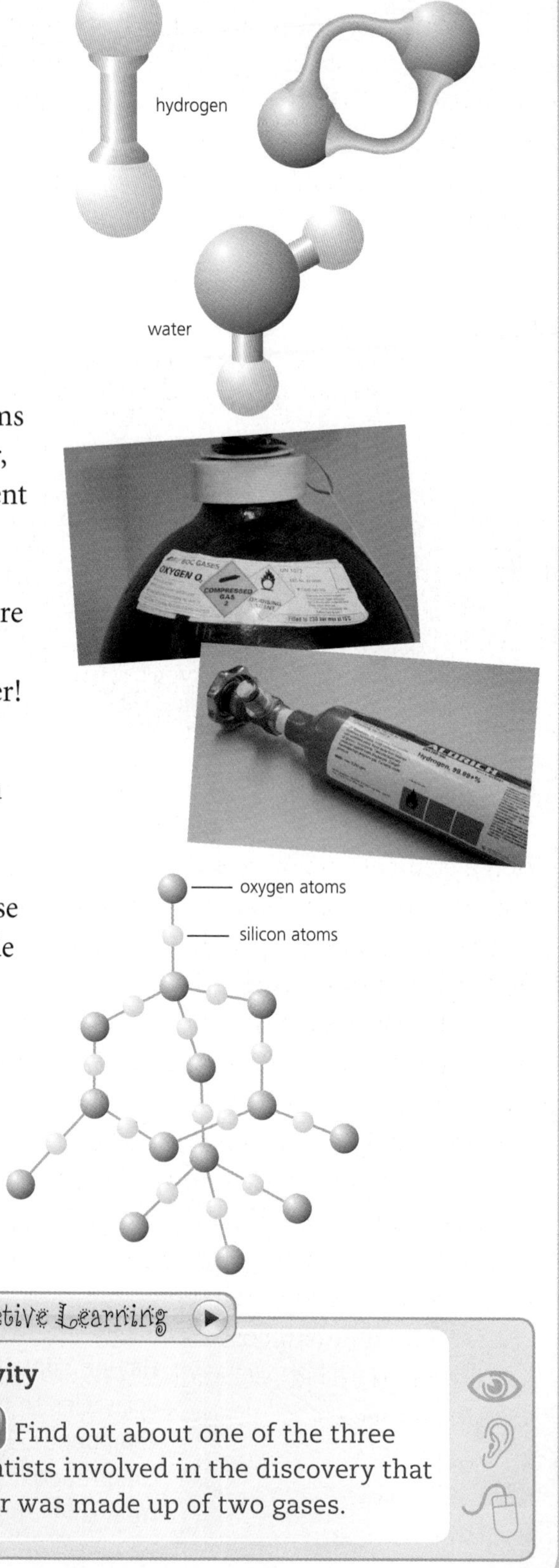

QUESTIONS

1 a) List all of the elements mentioned since the start of the chapter.

b) Use a Periodic Table to find the symbols of the elements mentioned.

2 Explain fully why sodium is an element yet salt is not.

3 Water is described as a 'colourless liquid'. Can you think of two other properties of water?

Active Learning

Activity

Find out about one of the three scientists involved in the discovery that water was made up of two gases.

Elements and compounds in the First World War

On 22 April 1915, allied soldiers fighting the Germans in the First World War noticed a green haze sweeping over the battlefields as evening fell. Chaos descended on the trenches as people began to struggle for breath. The German soldiers were using chlorine gas in an act of chemical warfare. The effects of such a poisonous element were horrific, leading to the deaths of many allied soldiers.

One of the interesting things about the Periodic Table of the elements is the different properties of the elements. Some elements, such as chlorine, are toxic, yet other elements, such as oxygen, are responsible for keeping all living things alive. Perhaps even more fascinating is the way in which elements like chlorine can be made completely safe by joining them to another element. For example, when sodium is joined to chlorine, an explosive reaction takes place and the compound sodium chloride is formed. Sodium chloride is table salt! We all eat salt either by deliberately adding it to our food or by eating the hundreds of foods that have salt added to them. Small amounts of either sodium or chlorine will harm, and possibly kill, a human being, yet small amounts of table salt are completely harmless. Sodium is a soft, grey coloured metal that reacts violently with water. Chlorine is a greenish-yellow gas which forms hydrochloric acid when added to water (hence the reason people can die from inhaling chlorine). Sodium chloride is a white solid that simply dissolves in water. This illustrates how the properties of compounds are often very different from their elements.

The interesting properties of elements and compounds allow them to be used by humans on a daily basis. For example, the toxic nature of chlorine is useful when chlorine is added to water to make it safe to drink. **Chlorinated** water was first used in 1897 during an outbreak of **typhoid** in England. Chlorine was shown to kill the bacteria that caused typhoid and it was believed that the chlorination of water supplies in 1897 helped to stop the spread of typhoid in England. To this day, chlorine and compounds of chlorine are used to disinfect water supplies all over the world.

QUESTIONS

1. Make a list of five elements that are essential for human survival and explain what each element is used for.
2. Describe two compounds other than water and salt, and explain how they are different from the elements that they are made from.

Active Learning

Activities

1 Imagine you are a scientist working during the First World War. You have been asked to design a mask that will stop soldiers inhaling chlorine gas. Research methods that were used to stop chlorine gas and use this information to draw a design for a mask.

2 Debate: should chemicals such as chlorine be allowed to be used as weapons of war?

3 Find out about water chlorination and the **cholera** outbreak of 1991 in Peru. Produce a news article explaining what happened.

4 Draw a cartoon to teach that elements are different from the compounds that they are made from.

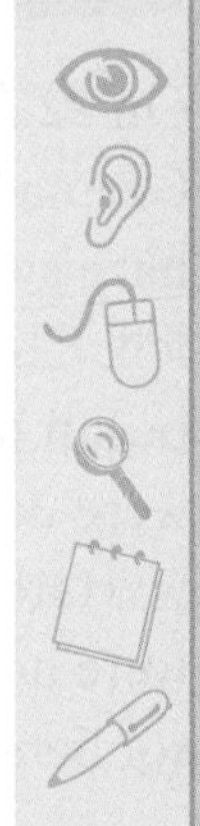

Elements, compounds and mixtures

The simple act of breathing is amazing! We don't think about it, but those breaths in and out keep us alive and well. The air we breathe is not an element or a compound, but a mixture of elements and compounds. Air contains the elements nitrogen and oxygen as well as other elements in small amounts. Air also contains the compounds carbon dioxide and water. It is for this reason that air is usually called a mixture. A mixture is different from a compound as the substances in a mixture are not joined together.

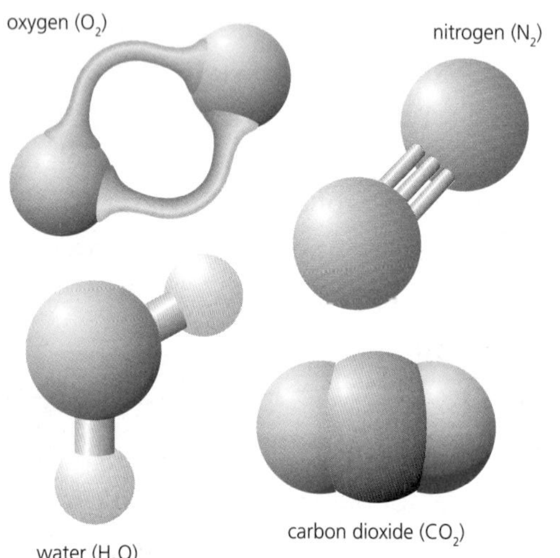

Simple mixtures in the lab can help us appreciate the difference between elements, compounds and mixtures. Consider the elements iron and sulphur.

They are very different elements. Iron is a silvery grey metal which can be moved using a magnet. It is very strong and must be heated to 1535 °C to melt. Sulphur is a bright yellow solid non-metal which is brittle, not magnetic and can be melted by placing in the flame of a candle.

A lump of iron and iron filings.

A lump of sulphur and sulphur powder.

If some iron filings and sulphur powder are added to a test tube and shaken, a mixture of iron and sulphur is formed. The iron can easily be separated from the sulphur by using a magnet to attract the iron.

Elements, compounds and mixtures

If a test tube containing a mixture of iron filings and powdered sulphur is heated strongly, the compound iron sulphide is formed. Once this is made, the iron can no longer be separated from the sulphur with a magnet as the two elements are now chemically joined together.

The differences between elements, compounds and mixtures can be understood by comparing the substances to a packet of dolly mixtures. If you select two types of dolly mixtures, these represent the atoms of iron and sulphur. If you mix them up by shaking the sweets, they can still be easily separated. However, if you heat the sweets strongly, you form a sticky mess where all the sweets (atoms) are joined. It's much more difficult to separate them!

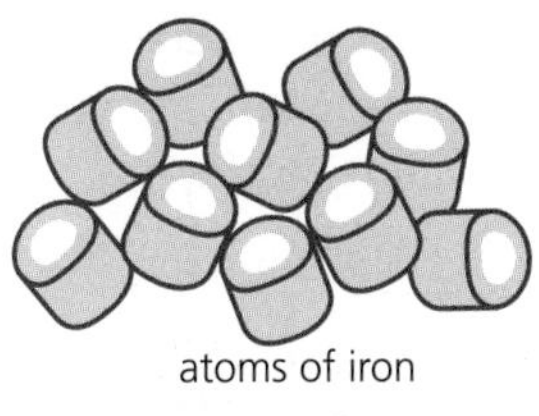
atoms of iron

atoms of sulphur

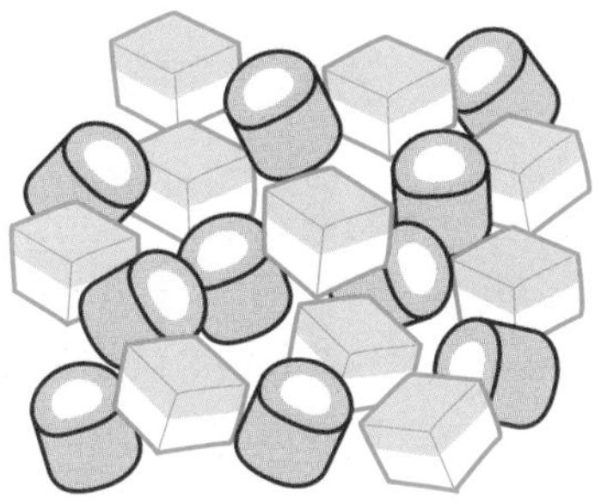

Active Learning

Activities

1 Find out about the gases in the air. List the names and percentages of all the gases in the air.

2 Carry out the iron and sulphur experiment to explore the difference between elements, mixtures and compounds.

Compound names and chemical formulae

Ask anyone the formula for water and they will no doubt be able to tell you the answer is H_2O! What does this actually mean? It tells us water is a compound of hydrogen and oxygen. It also tells us that one water molecule contains two hydrogen atoms joined to one oxygen atom. Chemists refer to water as hydrogen oxide.

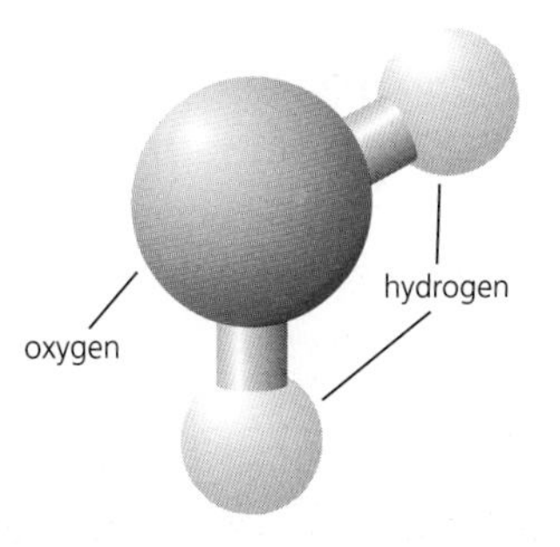

You have come across many compound names in this chapter already: carbon dioxide is one of the gases you breathe out. It is also found in carbonated soft drinks and is believed to be one of the gases responsible

Compound names and chemical formulae

for global warming. It contains the elements carbon and oxygen. The formula for carbon dioxide is CO_2, telling us that one molecule of carbon dioxide contains one carbon atom and two oxygen atoms.

The name of a compound tells us the elements present. There are two simple rules that help us to work out the elements present:

- If the name of the compound ends in –ide, the compound contains two elements.
- If the name of the compound ends in –ite or –ate, the compound contains two elements plus oxygen.

This is illustrated in the table below:

Name of compound	Elements present
Calcium phosphide	Calcium and phosphorus
Sulphur chloride	Sulphur and chlorine
Copper carbonate	Copper, carbon and oxygen
Lithium sulphite	Lithium, sulphur and oxygen

QUESTIONS

1. Draw a table like the one on the left and complete the names of the elements present in the following compounds: sodium carbonate, lead oxide, nitrogen hydride, potassium nitrate and sulphur dioxide.
2. Suggest names for compounds which contain a) lead and sulphur, b) zinc and oxygen, c) magnesium, sulphur and oxygen and d) silver and chlorine
3. Copy and complete the following table to work out the number and type of atoms present in the compound whose formula is shown. The first example has been done for you.

Formula	Atoms present
CO_2	One carbon and two oxygen atoms
PCl_5	
NH_4Cl	
H_2SO_4	
	One sulphur and two oxygen atoms
	Two nitrogen and four oxygen atoms

Active Learning

Activities

1. Look at the label on a soft drink container or bottle of shampoo. List two of the compounds and state the elements present in the compounds.
2. Find out about a compound listed on a label on something at home. Find out what the compound is used for and state the elements it contains.
3. Look up the formula for the following chemicals and state the number of each type of atom present.

   a) sugar (sucrose)

   b) alcohol (ethanol)

   c) nitrogen

   d) methane.

Oxygen: the compound maker

It is difficult to imagine our world without oxygen. It is found in water as part of a compound and is present as an element in the air. It is, quite simply, the element which keeps most living things alive. To a chemist, oxygen is a very reactive gas that forms compounds with many elements. Many of these chemical reactions can be carried out in the laboratory. Look at the following:

- When a piece of magnesium is heated in air, the magnesium reacts spectacularly with oxygen from the air to form the compound magnesium oxide.

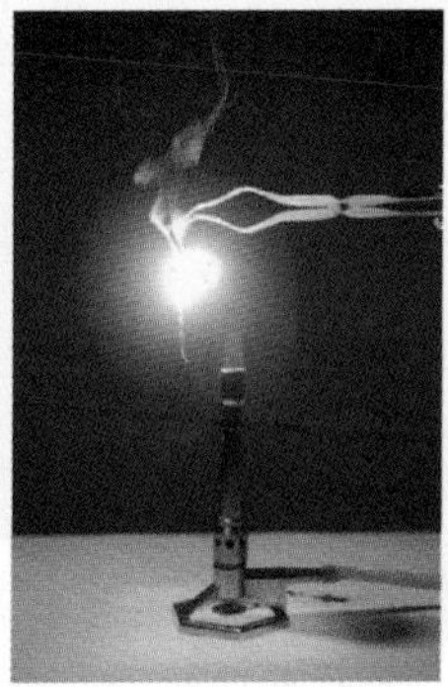

- When a lump of sulphur is heated in a gas jar of pure oxygen, the poisonous gas sulphur dioxide is formed.

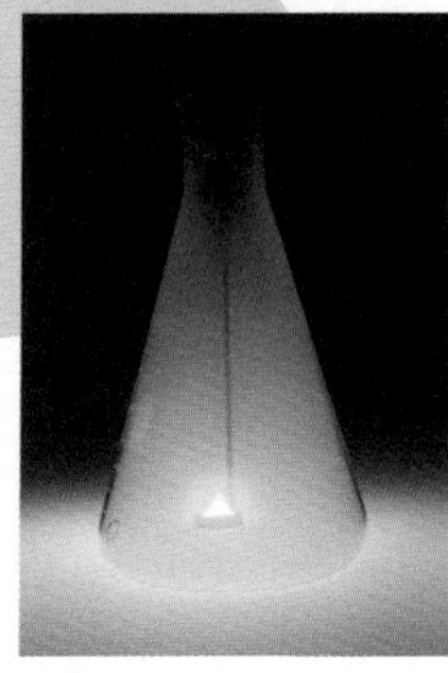

- When carbon powder is lit in a gas jar of oxygen, carbon dioxide is formed.

Oxygen: the compound maker

The previous examples illustrate the many compounds that can be formed by reacting elements with oxygen. Many of these chemical reactions can be observed in everyday life. For example, when iron is exposed to air, rust is formed. Rust is simply another example of oxygen's ability to form compounds with other elements; rust is iron oxide.

Chemists often prefer to use word equations to simplify what is happening in a chemical reaction. Rather than describe a reaction using lots of words, as you can see in the previous examples, word equations simply show what is reacting and what is formed e.g.

Magnesium + oxygen → magnesium oxide

Carbon + oxygen → carbon dioxide

Sulphur + oxygen → sulphur dioxide

The substances on the left-hand side of the arrow are known as the reactants. The substances on the right-hand side of the arrow are known as the products.

QUESTIONS

1 Write word equations for the following chemical reactions:
   a) Hydrogen reacts with oxygen to form water.
   b) Copper reacts with chlorine to form copper chloride
   c) Calcium carbonate reacts with hydrochloric acid to form calcium chloride, water and carbon dioxide.
   d) Iron oxide is formed from iron reacting with oxygen.
2 Label the reactants and products in the above equations.

Breaking down compounds

The sight of blood is enough to make some people faint! The familiar red colour of blood is caused by a compound of iron present in red blood cells. This iron compound is essential as it helps to transport oxygen around the body. If the sight of red blood makes you feel ill, how would you feel if you saw blue blood? You're unlikely to encounter this unless you happen to squash a squid or cut open an octopus!

These organisms have blue blood, as do other creatures such as oysters, snails, certain crabs and spiders. The difference in colour is caused by a compound of the element copper. The copper compound is present, instead of an iron compound, to transport oxygen around the body of these creatures. Copper is an element that you are probably very familiar with. It is a shiny brown coloured metal and it is commonly used to make pipes for carrying water. As it has many uses, scientists have developed methods to get copper from compounds which contain copper.

Solid copper and copper carbonate.

Breaking down compounds

Copper can be extracted from the compound copper carbonate by heating it strongly to produce copper oxide and carbon dioxide. This can be shown as a word equation:

Copper carbonate → copper oxide + carbon dioxide

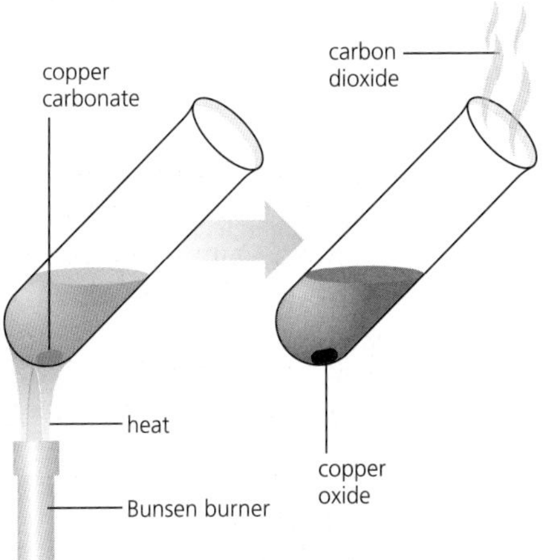

If the copper oxide is then heated with carbon, copper and carbon dioxide are produced:

Copper oxide + carbon → copper + carbon dioxide

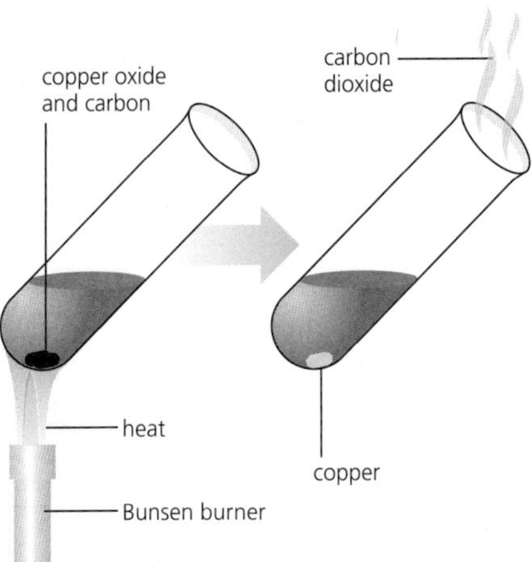

Obtaining copper from a compound of copper is not a simple process. This is generally true for obtaining most elements from their compounds. Think about water. It is a compound containing hydrogen joined to oxygen, yet how often have you seen these two gases coming from water? The reason it is so difficult to obtain elements from compounds is because the elements are chemically joined. The chemical join in a compound is usually known as a bond. To break up compounds usually requires a massive amount of energy to break up the strong chemical bond.

So how are elements obtained from a compound? Sometimes, as in the example of breaking down copper carbonate, simply heating to a high enough temperature, often in the presence of another element, is enough to break up the compound. But this does not always work. No matter how much you heat water, it will not break down into hydrogen and oxygen as the bond between these two elements is far too strong. To break down water, a process known as **electrolysis** is used. This involves passing electricity through a compound and using the energy in the electricity to break down the compound into its elements. This process is used in industry to obtain many useful elements from compounds. For example, chlorine gas is obtained from the electrolysis of sodium chloride. Aluminium is obtained by the electrolysis of aluminium compounds.

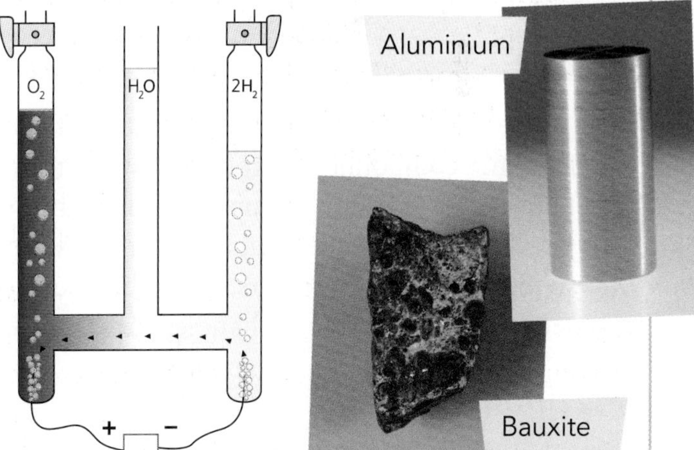

Electrolysis can be carried out in the laboratory. If a small sample of copper chloride is dissolved in water and placed in a beaker containing carbon electrodes connected to an electricity supply, the

Breaking down compounds

copper chloride will start to break down. One of the electrodes will become covered in brown copper and chlorine gas will be seen bubbling at the other electrode. The smell of chlorine also becomes obvious.

Copper chloride.

QUESTIONS

1 Name the elements present in copper carbonate.

2 Write a word equation which shows the reactants and products when (a) water is broken down by electrolysis and (b) copper chloride is broken down by electrolysis.

3 Explain fully why lots of energy is needed to break down a compound.

4 Look at a sample of copper carbonate and a sample of copper. List the differences between the element and its compound.

Active Learning

Activities

1 Break down copper chloride in the laboratory by electrolysis.

2 Find out about the electrolysis of aluminium compounds.

Using elements and compounds in everyday life

One of the fascinating aspects of chemistry is finding new uses for elements and compounds. Throughout your study of chemistry you will meet the elements and the compounds they can form, and you will be surprised by the properties that they exhibit. Many of these properties are life saving whereas many others, as you have just learned, can cause death if an element or compound is handled incorrectly.

Platinum and its compounds

Platinum is a very expensive metal that has become popular to wear as jewellery e.g. as rings and chains.

Apart from jewellery, it has many uses both as an element and as a compound. Another common use of the element is in a car's exhaust as the catalytic converter. It is also mixed with other metals to produce components for the electronics industry e.g. hard disk drives in computers often contain a mixture of cobalt and platinum.

Using elements and compounds in everyday life

Compounds of platinum are quite rare, but one of them is used as a medicine to treat cancer. **Cisplatin** ($PtCl_2N_2H_6$) has been used to treat cancers since the 1970s and has been altered over the years to create other platinum compounds which are just as effective but produce fewer side effects. Cisplatin was one of the drugs that were used to save the life of the world famous Tour de France cycling champion Lance Armstrong who developed cancer as a young athlete.

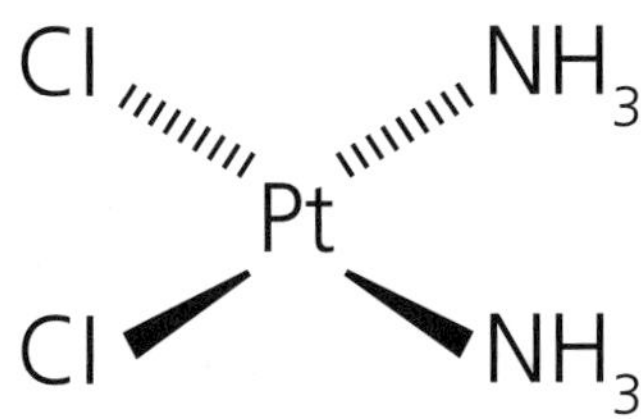

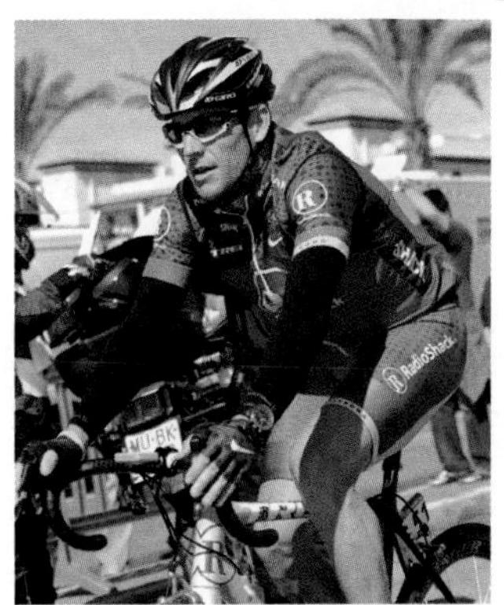

Phosphorus and its compounds

One of the themes running through this chapter is that the properties of compounds can be very different from their elements. Phosphorus and its compounds are good examples of this.

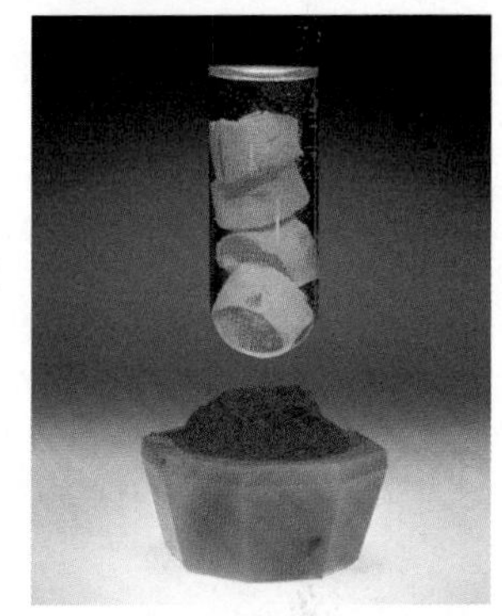

Phosphorus exists in two main forms which are named after their appearance: white and red phosphorus.

White phosphorus is extremely reactive and is usually stored under water to prevent it reacting with oxygen. It received lots of media attention in January 2009 when it was reported that the Israeli army was using white phosphorus bombs against the Palestinians.

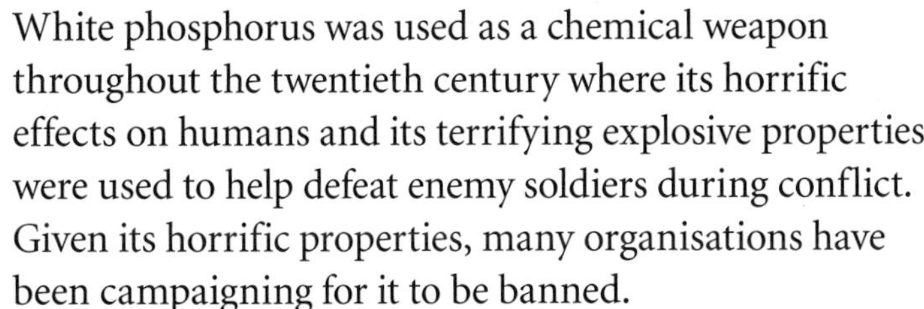

White phosphorus was used as a chemical weapon throughout the twentieth century where its horrific effects on humans and its terrifying explosive properties were used to help defeat enemy soldiers during conflict. Given its horrific properties, many organisations have been campaigning for it to be banned.

There are many compounds of phosphorus, including phosphoric acid (H_3PO_4). This is added to soft drinks (look at the ingredients of a can of lemonade or coke) to improve the flavour and to prevent unwanted organisms growing in the sugary solution. Unlike phosphorus, dilute phosphoric acid can be consumed without causing explosions in your mouth, although it will accelerate tooth decay! Other uses of phosphorus compounds include phosphates in washing powders and in toothpastes.

QUESTIONS

Name the elements present in:

(a) cisplatin and (b) phosphoric acid.

Active Learning

Activities

1  Find out how much 1 kg of platinum costs and compare this to 1 kg of gold.

2 Find out what cisplatin is used to treat and some of the side effects associated with the medicine.

3 Find out why armies are still allowed to use white phosphorus.

4 Debate: should white phosphorus be banned?

5 Debate: should warning labels be put on soft drinks to warn people about the dangers of tooth decay?

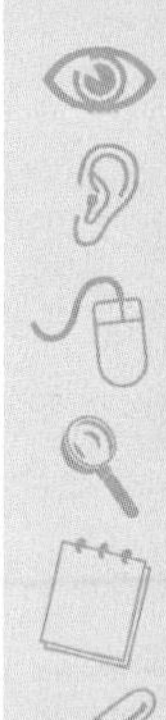

GLOSSARY

Electrolysis a process which uses electricity to separate a compound into its elements

Element a simple substance that contains only one type of atom

Compound two or more elements chemically joined together

Chlorinated where chlorine has been added to a substance

Cholera a disease caused by bacteria found in water which causes severe diarrhoea and can lead to death

Cisplatin a drug used to treat cancer which contains the element platinum

Typhoid a disease caused by drinking contaminated water or eating contaminated food. It causes a high fever and can lead to death

MATERIALS

Properties and Uses of Substances

3

The Periodic Table

Level 2 What came before?

SCN 2-15a

By contributing to investigations into familiar changes in substances to produce other substances, I can describe how their characteristics have changed.

Level 3 What is this chapter about?

SCN 3-15a

I have developed my knowledge of the Periodic Table by considering the properties and uses of a variety of elements relative to their positions.

The Periodic Table

In this chapter you will learn more about the unique substances called elements – substances made of only one type of atom. Everything that you see is made from **elements**, even you! There are just over 100 different elements but there is an enormous variety of possible combinations of these elements. Millions in fact! It is these different combinations of elements that make everything around you. Elements are the basic building blocks of the whole world.

Ancient Greek philosophers thought that there were only four elements – earth, air, fire and water. This was despite them knowing about copper, gold, iron, lead, mercury, silver and tin. To the ancient Greeks, these were just metals!

In the 1700s scientists became able to do experiments and started to use the word element in a different way. To them, an element was a substance which could not be broken down by existing chemical methods. In the late 1700s 33 elements were believed to exist. A French scientist, Antoine Lavoisier, arranged them into four groups called gases, non-metals, metals and earths. This was one of the first attempts to find some sort of pattern among the elements. He included hydrogen and oxygen in the gases group, but also light and heat, which are forms of energy, not elements!

In the early 1800s the invention of the battery led to the discovery of more elements, including potassium which was made from a substance called potash which Lavoisier had thought was an element itself because he could not break it down. Humphrey Davy did break it down using electricity. He is credited with discovering six elements, including chlorine and iodine. It is believed that his work with these toxic chemicals led to his early death at the age of 50 in 1829.

Humphrey Davy also invented the Davy Lamp in 1815. This reduced the risk for miners working in mines with flammable gases.

Through the 1800s the number of elements discovered continued to grow, and scientists wondered if there would be an infinite number of them. However, there was still no obvious pattern within them.

By now scientists had changed their ideas of what an element was again, to more like what they believe today. Each element was made from its own type of atom, and atoms of different elements had different weights. Some scientists thought a pattern could be produced by arranging the elements in order of increasing atomic weight. Others believed that the chemical properties of the elements would be the key.

Shown here is Dmitri Mendeleev, the inventor of the Periodic Table. He had one haircut every year but only when the weather was warm!

In February 1869, a Russian scientist named Dmitri Mendeleev wrote the symbol and atomic weight of each element onto separate pieces of paper. At that time 63 elements were known. He then spent three days and nights trying to group them together in clusters with similar chemical properties. It was a bit like playing a game of cards today with many of the 52 playing cards missing! Eventually he fell asleep, and the basis of the modern Periodic Table came to him in a dream! The key idea was to lay the cards out in a certain order, but to leave spaces for cards which could be written out as more new elements were discovered in the future. He was so sure that he was right that he was able to predict the properties of undiscovered elements. His predictions were eventually confirmed as more elements were discovered.

			Ti = 50	Zr = 90	? = 180
			V = 51	Nb = 94	Ta = 182
			Cr = 52	Mo = 96	W = 186
			Mn = 55	Rh = 104,4	Pt = 197,4
			Fe = 56	Ru = 104,4	Ir = 198
			Ni = Co = 59	Pd = 106,6	Os = 199
H = 1			Cu = 63,4	Ag = 108	Hg = 200
	Be = 9,4	Mg = 24	Zn = 65,2	Cd = 112	
	B = 11	Al = 27,4	? = 68	Ur = 116	Au = 197?
	C = 12	Si = 28	? = 70	Sn = 118	Bi = 210?
	N = 14	P = 31	As = 75	Sb = 122	
	O = 16	S = 32	Se = 79,4	Te = 128?	
	F = 19	Cl = 35,5	Br = 80	I = 127	
Li = 7	Na = 23	K = 39	Rb = 85,4	Cs = 133	Tl = 204
		Ca = 40	Sr = 87,6	Ba = 137	Pb = 207
		? = 45	Ce = 92		
		?Er = 56	La = 94		
		?Yt = 60	Di = 95		
		?In = 75,6	Th = 118?		

This was Mendeleev's first attempt at grouping elements together in the Periodic Table.

It took another two years or so for Mendeleev to produce a Periodic Table which looks pretty much like the ones on the walls of most school science labs today. The science community at that time was amazed at how accurate the new table was.

Mendeleev continued to develop his Periodic Table and produced this second version.

Period	Group I	Group II	Group III	Group IV	Group V	Group VI	Group VII	Group VIII
1	H = 1							
2	Li = 7	Be = 9,4	B = 11	C = 12	N = 14	O = 16	F = 19	
3	Na = 23	Mg = 24	Al = 27,3	Si = 28	P = 31	5 = 32	Cl = 35,5	
4	K = 39	Ca = 40	— = 44	Ti = 48	V = 51	Cr = 52	Mn = 55	Fe = 56, Co = 59, Ni = 59, Cu = 63.
5	(Cu = 63)	Zn = 65	— = 68	— = 72	Aa = 75	So = 78	Br = 80	
6	Rb = 85	Sr = 87	?Yt = 88	Zr = 90	Nb = 94	Mo = 96	— = 100	Ru = 104, Rh = 104, Pd = 106, Ag = 108
7	(Ag = 108)	Cd = 112	In = 113	So = 118	Sb = 122	Tc = 125	J = 127	
8	Co = 133	Ba = 137	?Di = 138	?Co = 140	—	—	—	— — —
9	(—)	—	—	—	—	—	—	
10	—	—	?Et = 178	?La = 180	Ta = 182	W = 184	—	Os = 195, Ir = 197, Pt = 198, Au = 199.
11	(Au = 199)	Hg = 200	Tl = 204	Pb = 207	Bi = 208	—	—	— — —
12	—	—	—	Th = 231	—	C = 240	—	

QUESTIONS

1 Imagine that you are a scientist and you have just discovered a new element. What name and symbol would you give to this element? Explain your choice.

2 Copy and complete the following sentences:

Chemists have classified elements by arranging them in the _______ _______.

There are over ____ elements and they are arranged in ________. All the elements in each group have similar _________ _______.

3 Pick any element from the Periodic Table and do some research on that element. Your report should answer questions such as when it was discovered, its uses, properties and where it can be found.

Since Mendeleev produced the first Periodic Table, many new elements have been discovered, but they still fit into the table that he produced all those years ago. Some of the most recently discovered elements are named after famous scientists. Mendeleev himself has one named after him – Mendelevium (Md).

Periodic Table of the Elements

																		2 Helium **He**
3 Lithium **Li**	4 Berllium **Be**	Atomic number Name of element Symbol							1 Hydrogen **H**				5 Boron **B**	6 Carbon **C**	7 Nitrogen **N**	8 Oxygen **O**	9 Fluorine **F**	10 Neon **Ne**
11 Sodium **Na**	12 Magnesium **Mg**												13 Aluminum **Al**	14 Silicon **Si**	15 Phosphorus **P**	16 Sulphur **S**	17 Chlorine **Cl**	18 Argon **Ar**
19 Potassium **K**	20 Calcium **Ca**	21 Scandium **Sc**		22 Titanium **Ti**	23 Vanadium **V**	24 Chromium **Cr**	25 Manganese **Mn**	26 Iron **Fe**	27 Cobalt **Co**	28 Nickel **Ni**	29 Copper **Cu**	30 Zinc **Zn**	31 Gallium **Ga**	32 Germanium **Ge**	33 Arsenic **As**	34 Selenium **Se**	35 Bromine **Br**	36 Krypton **Kr**
37 Rubidium **RB**	38 Strontium **Sr**	39 Yttrium **Y**		40 Zirconium **Zr**	41 Niobium **Nb**	42 Molyb-denum **Mu**	43 Technetium **Tc**	44 Ruthenium **Ru**	45 Rhodium **Rh**	46 Palladium **Pd**	47 Silver **Ag**	48 Cadmium **Cd**	49 Indium **In**	50 Tin **Sn**	51 Antimony **Sb**	52 Tellurium **Te**	53 Iodine **I**	54 Xenon **Xe**
55 Caesium **Cs**	56 Barium **Ba**	57 Lanthanum **La**	58–71 ●	72 Hafnium **Hf**	73 Tantalum **Ta**	74 Tungsten **W**	75 Rhenium **Re**	76 Osmium **Os**	77 Iridium **Ir**	78 Platinum **Pt**	79 Gold **Au**	80 Mercury **Hg**	81 Thallium **Tl**	82 Lead **Pb**	83 Bismuth **Bi**	84 Polonium **Po**	85 Astatine **At**	86 Radon **Rn**
87 Francium **Fr**	88 Radium **Ra**	89 Actinium **Ac**	90–103 ■	104 Ruther-fordium **Rf**	105 Dubnium **Db**	106 Seaborgium **Sg**	107 Bohrium **Bh**	108 Hassium **Hs**	109 Meitnerium **Mt**									

●	58 Cerium **Ce**	59 Praseodymium **Pr**	60 Neodymium **Nd**	61 Promethium **Pm**	62 Samarium **Sm**	63 Europium **Eu**	64 Gadolinium **Gd**	65 Terbium **Tb**	66 Dysprosium **Dy**	67 Holmium **Ho**	68 Erbium **Er**	69 Thulium **Tm**	70 Ytterbium **Yb**	71 Lutetium **Lu**
■	90 Thorium **Th**	91 Protactinium **Pa**	92 Uranium **U**	93 Neptunium **Np**	94 Plutonium **Pu**	95 Americium **Am**	96 Curium **Cm**	97 Berkelium **Bk**	98 Californium **Cf**	99 Einsteinium **Es**	100 Fermium **Fm**	101 Mendelevium **Md**	102 Nobelium **No**	103 Lawrencium **Lr**

This is the modern Periodic Table that we use today.

Elements: the building blocks

Everything in the world is made from elements but if we could look very closely at an element we would see that an element is made from tiny particles called **atoms**. Atoms are very small. They are so small that we can't actually see them. It is hard to imagine just how small they are but the picture shown below may help.

This is a single grain of sand. How many atoms do you think are in the grain of sand? 100, 1000 or even 10000? In a grain of sand there are approximately 78 000 000 000 000 000 000 atoms!

In a pure element all the atoms are the same. **Elements are substances that are made up of only one type of atom and cannot be broken down any further.**

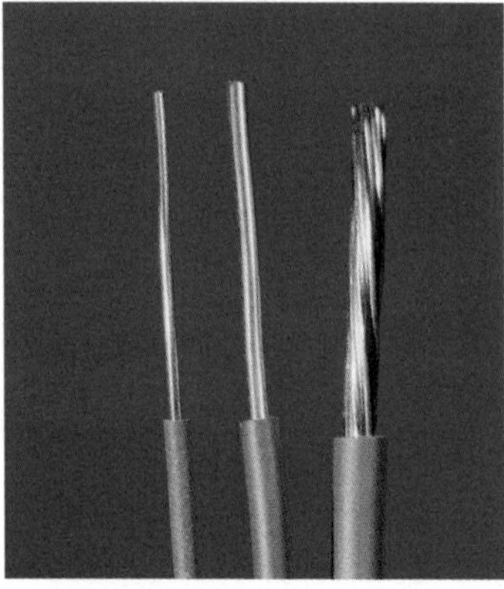

The wires shown here are made from copper which is an element. That means that they contain only one type of atom. If we could look at the atoms that the wires are made of, we would see that all the atoms are the same.

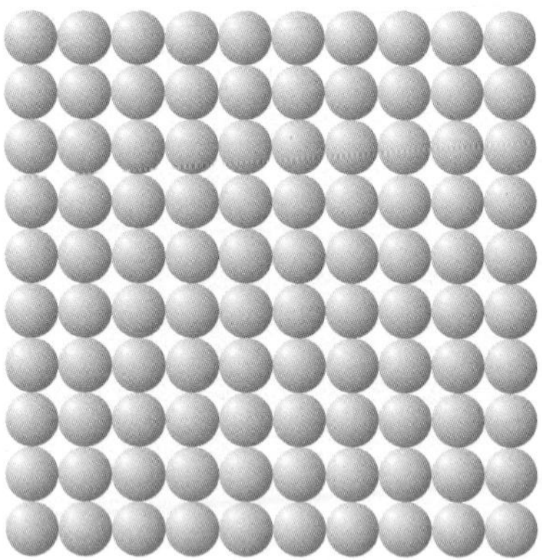

The photo of the grain of sand was not taken with the kind of microscope you have in school! If we looked at a different object that is not made from a pure element using the same microscope, we would see a very different picture.

Here are six boxes showing the atoms in various substances but which of the substances can be classed as an element?

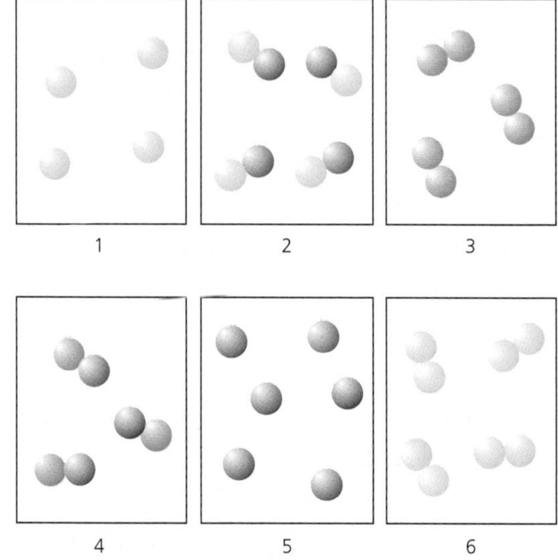

Boxes 1, 3, 5 and 6 all contain elements, because they contain only one type of atom.

What do boxes 2 and 4 contain? They are not elements because all the atoms are not the same.

These are called **compounds**. Compounds are formed when two or more different elements react together. Your teacher may let you react two elements together to produce a compound. For example, if you burn some magnesium, the magnesium atoms combine with the oxygen atoms from the air to form a white compound called magnesium oxide.

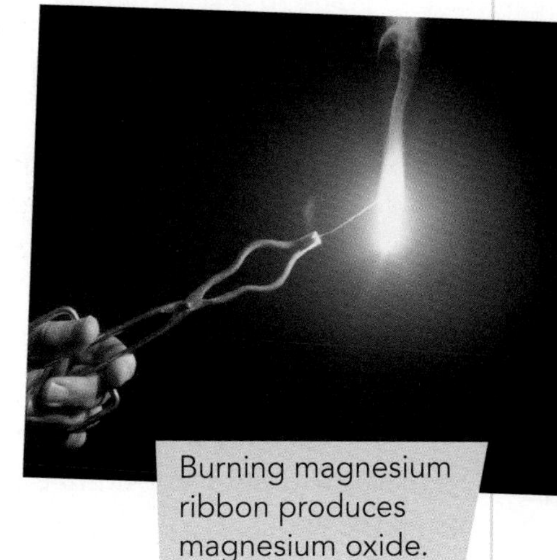

Burning magnesium ribbon produces magnesium oxide.

Compounds are made up of two or more different elements chemically joined together. There are millions of compounds that can be made by reacting elements together. Think about it – there are only 26 letters in the alphabet but the English language has hundreds of thousands of words, all of which are made from combinations of these 26 letters. There are over 100 elements in the Periodic Table so just imagine the number of compounds that can be made by combining them!

QUESTIONS

1 Copy the boxes showing the groups of atoms opposite into your jotter and use the descriptions from the box below to label each picture.

> Atoms of one element
>
> A **mixture** of two elements
>
> One compound
>
> A mixture of two compounds
>
> A mixture of an element and a compound
>
> Molecules of an element

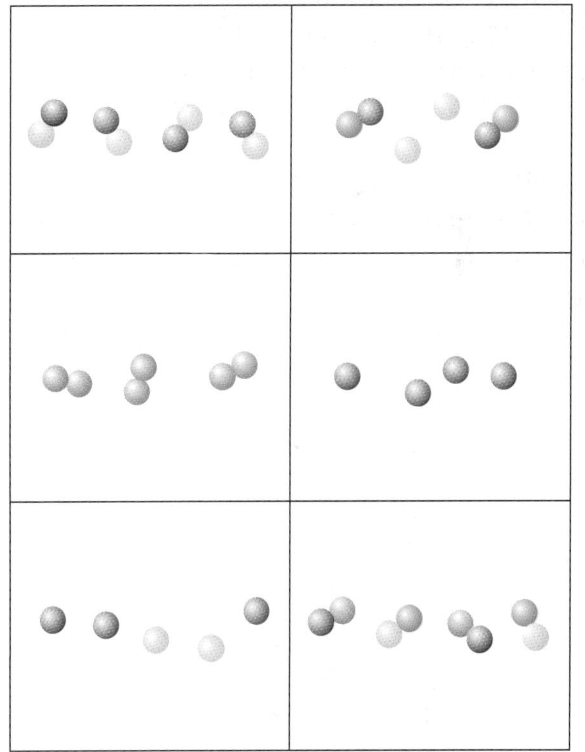

2 Listed below are a variety of substances. Sort the substances into a table with the headings 'Elements' and 'Compounds'.

sulphur, carbon dioxide, aluminium, sodium, water, magnesium, magnesium oxide, copper and calcium carbonate.

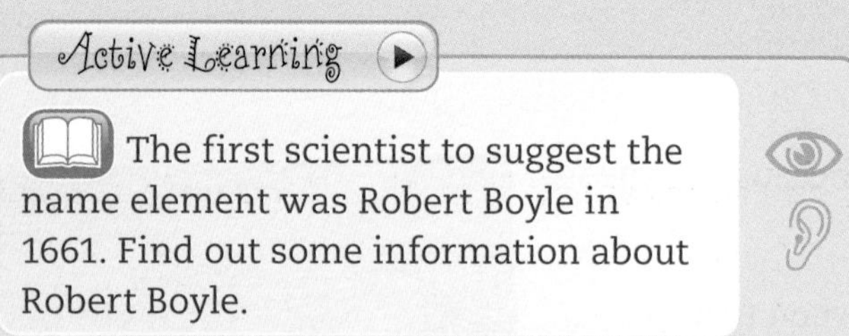

The first scientist to suggest the name element was Robert Boyle in 1661. Find out some information about Robert Boyle.

Element symbols

Scientists use symbols to represent elements as it can make the elements a lot easier to work with on paper. Imagine trying to do a fairly simple sum in maths without using numbers or symbols but using the words. For example:

Eight hundred plus one hundred and forty four equals nine hundred and forty four. If this is multiplied by two then the answer is one thousand eight hundred and eighty eight.

If the same sum is done using the correct numbers and symbols then the sum becomes much clearer and therefore simpler:

$800 + 144 = 944$

$944 \times 2 = 1888$.

This is why chemists use symbols to represent elements and chemical formulae.

There are over 100 elements in the Periodic Table and each one has its own symbol. The very first scientists gave elements symbols but they were very complicated. For example, gold had the symbol:

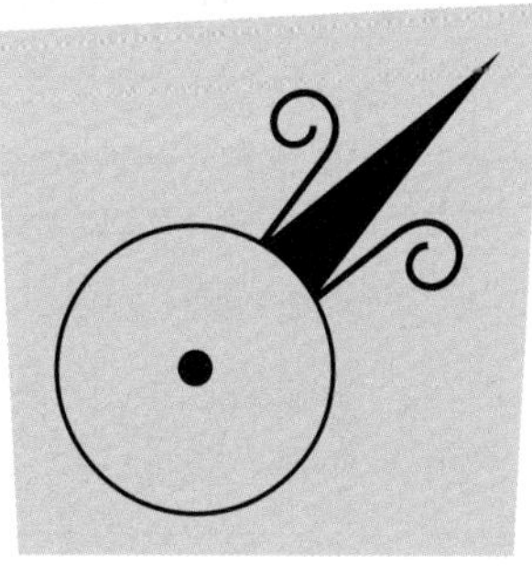

And copper had the symbol:

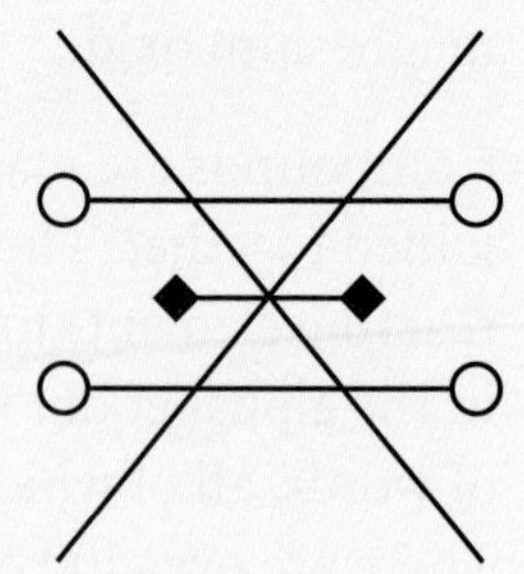

These symbols were very difficult to work with.

Today, however, scientists have much simpler symbols for all the known chemical elements. For example gold and copper today have the symbols:

Gold **Au**	Copper **Cu**

The symbols Au and Cu come from the Latin words for the elements – **Au**rum and **Cu**prum. Some are a bit more straightforward such as **F**luorine and **Ne**on:

Fluorine **F**	Neon **Ne**

The symbols are used to produce chemical formulae for compounds. Chemical formulae tell us how many atoms are present in a substance. For example, fluorine has the formula F_2. This tells us that one **molecule** of fluorine contains two fluorine atoms. Molecules are made up of two or more atoms held together by strong bonds.

If all the atoms in a molecule are identical then it is a molecule of an element.

Element symbols

Some other examples are shown below:

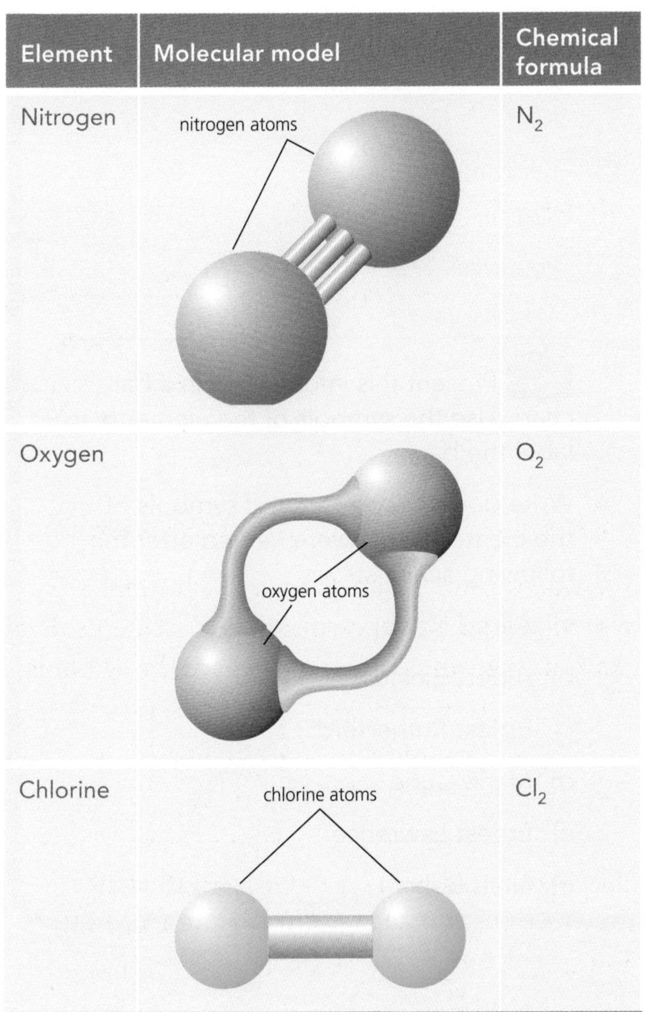

Element	Molecular model	Chemical formula
Nitrogen		N_2
Oxygen		O_2
Chlorine		Cl_2

If the atoms are different then it is a molecule of a compound.

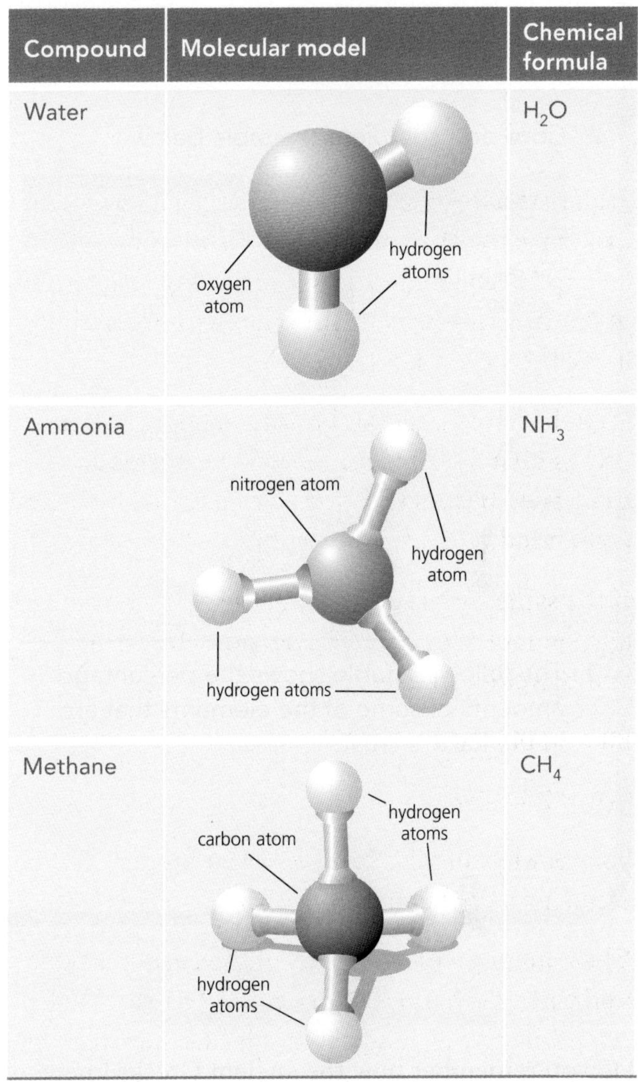

Compound	Molecular model	Chemical formula
Water		H_2O
Ammonia		NH_3
Methane		CH_4

The chemical formulae shown in the tables use the symbols of the elements as a kind of chemical shorthand. They are used to represent elements but they are also used to represent the elements that are contained in compounds.

Scientists use chemical formulae every day to represent many elements and compounds.

QUESTIONS

1 Copy and complete the table below using the names and symbols of the first ten elements.

Element	Symbol

2 Copy and complete the table below.

Name	Formula	Number of each type of atom
Magnesium oxide	MgO	1 magnesium, 1 oxygen
Calcium chloride	$CaCl_2$	
Sodium oxide		2 sodium, 1 oxygen
Magnesium fluoride	MgF_2	
Calcium sulphide		1 calcium, 1 sulphur

3 The following table shows the percentage amounts of some of the elements that are in the Earth's crust.

Element	Percentage %
Oxygen	47
Silicon	25
Aluminium	8
Iron	5
Calcium	4
Sodium	4
Potassium	2
Magnesium	2

Present this information in a bar chart. Use the symbols of the elements to label the bars.

4 Write down the names and symbols of the elements that were named after the following scientists:

a) Alfred Nobel

b) Albert Einstein

c) Ernest Rutherford

d) Marie Curie

e) Ernest Lawrence

d) Niels Bohr.

Metals and non-metals

Do you remember how the ancient Greeks knew about copper, gold, iron, lead, mercury, silver and tin, but dismissed them as 'just metals'? Today we know that most of the elements are metals. There are only 22 which are not. These metals are not randomly scattered throughout the Table. They are found towards one side of it, separated from the non-metals on the other side. Look at a Periodic Table in your class and see if you can see which side the metals are on. If you keep looking at the Periodic Table you may even be able to draw a line

on the table that separates the metals from non-metals. The one below shows exactly where this line should be:

Periodic Table of the Elements

Key: Atomic number / Name of element / Symbol

Transition metals

																		2 Helium **He**
3 Lithium **Li**	4 Berllium **Be**									1 Hydrogen **H**			5 Boron **B**	6 Carbon **C**	7 Nitrogen **N**	8 Oxygen **O**	9 Fluorine **F**	10 Neon **Ne**
11 Sodium **Na**	12 Magnesium **Mg**												13 Aluminum **Al**	14 Silicon **Si**	15 Phosphorus **P**	16 Sulphur **S**	17 Chlorine **Cl**	18 Argon **Ar**
19 Potassium **K**	20 Calcium **Ca**	21 Scandium **Sc**		22 Titanium **Ti**	23 Vanadium **V**	24 Chromium **Cr**	25 Manganese **Mn**	26 Iron **Fe**	27 Cobalt **Co**	28 Nickel **Ni**	29 Copper **Cu**	30 Zinc **Zn**	31 Gallium **Ga**	32 Germanium **Ge**	33 Arsenic **As**	34 Selenium **Se**	35 Bromine **Br**	36 Krypton **Kr**
37 Rubidium **RB**	38 Strontium **Sr**	39 Yttrium **Y**		40 Zirconium **Zr**	41 Niobium **Nb**	42 Molyb-denum **Mu**	43 Technetium **Tc**	44 Ruthenium **Ru**	45 Rhodium **Rh**	46 Palladium **Pd**	47 Silver **Ag**	48 Cadmium **Cd**	49 Indium **In**	50 Tin **Sn**	51 Antimony **Sb**	52 Tellurium **Te**	53 Iodine **I**	54 Xenon **Xe**
55 Caesium **Cs**	56 Barium **Ba**	57 Lanthanum **La**	58–71 ●	72 Hafnium **Hf**	73 Tantalum **Ta**	74 Tungsten **W**	75 Rhenium **Re**	76 Osmium **Os**	77 Iridium **Ir**	78 Platinum **Pt**	79 Gold **Au**	80 Mercury **Hg**	81 Thallium **Tl**	82 Lead **Pb**	83 Bismuth **Bi**	84 Polonium **Po**	85 Astatine **At**	86 Radon **Rn**
87 Francium **Fr**	88 Radium **Ra**	89 Actinium **Ac**	90–103 ■	104 Ruther-fordium **Rf**	105 Dubnium **Db**	106 Seaborgium **Sg**	107 Bohrium **Bh**	108 Hassium **Hs**	109 Meitnerium **Mt**									

zigzag line

●	58 Cerium **Ce**	59 Praseodymium **Pr**	60 Neodymium **Nd**	61 Promethium **Pm**	62 Samarium **Sm**	63 Europium **Eu**	64 Gadolinium **Gd**	65 Terbium **Tb**	66 Dysprosium **Dy**	67 Holmium **Ho**	68 Erbium **Er**	69 Thulium **Tm**	70 Ytterbium **Yb**	71 Lutetium **Lu**
■	90 Thorium **Th**	91 Protactinium **Pa**	92 Uranium **U**	93 Neptunium **Np**	94 Plutonium **Pu**	95 Americium **Am**	96 Curium **Cm**	97 Berkelium **Bk**	98 Californium **Cf**	99 Einsteinium **Es**	100 Fermium **Fm**	101 Mendelevium **Md**	102 Nobelium **No**	103 Lawrencium **Lr**

All the metals are on the left-hand side of the zigzag line and the non-metals are on the right. Imagine that you are given an unknown element; how would you decide if it is a metal or a non-metal? You could do this by testing some of the properties of the element.

Metals and non-metals

The table below shows some of the typical properties of metals and non-metals. Your teacher may let you test some of the properties listed below.

Property	Metal	Non-metal
Appearance	Shiny when polished	Dull if solid
Strength	Mostly strong	Weak if solid
Hardness	Mostly hard	Soft if solid
Density	High	Low in most cases
Melting and boiling point	High	Low in most cases
Conduction of heat	All good	Poor
Conduction of electricity	All good	Almost all are non-conductors

This table covers the properties of most of the metals and non-metals, but there are always exceptions. For example, mercury is a metal but it is a liquid at room temperature. Diamond is incredibly hard but is made from the non-metal element carbon. Sodium is a metal but you can cut it with a knife. Silicon is a non-metal but it has an extremely high melting point.

The uses of metals depend on their properties.

Aluminium is used to make the bodies of aeroplanes because it has a low **density**.

The Airbus A830 is a double decker airliner and is the largest passenger airliner in the world. It has enough seats for up to 853 passengers.

Gold is used for jewellery because it is very unreactive and looks good.

Copper is used for electrical cables because it is a very good conductor of electricity.

QUESTIONS

1 Of the 22 non-metal elements, 11 are solids, 1 is a liquid and 10 are gases at room temperature. Draw a table like the one below which shows this information.

2 John has found a sample of an unknown element. He records some of its properties in his lab book. He notes that it is a yellow solid, with a low density and does not conduct electricity. Is the unknown element a metal or a non-metal? Suggest what the element might be.

Element	Symbol	State at room temperature

Groups

The Periodic Table lists all the elements in an order which helps us understand why elements react as they do and what properties they might have. In the Periodic Table, some columns of elements are known as Groups. There are three Groups which we will look at in detail.

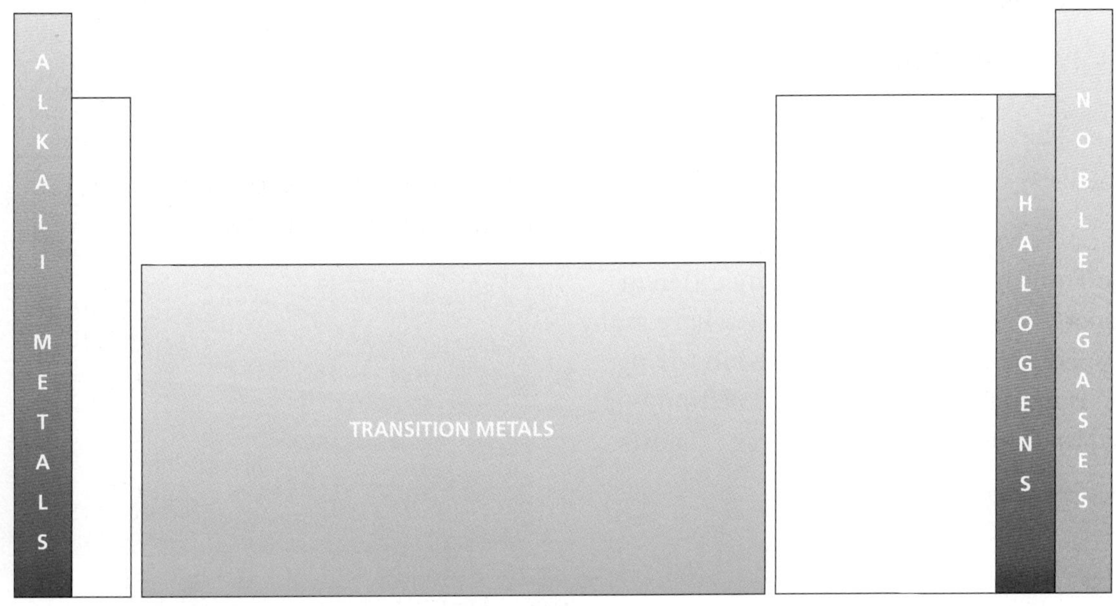

Groups

Alkali Metals (Group 1)

The **Alkali Metals** is a group of very reactive metals. They are so reactive that they even react with water. They are stored under oil so that they do not react with any moisture in the air. Your teacher may demonstrate the reactions of some of the alkali metals.

Sodium reacting with water.

Halogens (Group 7)

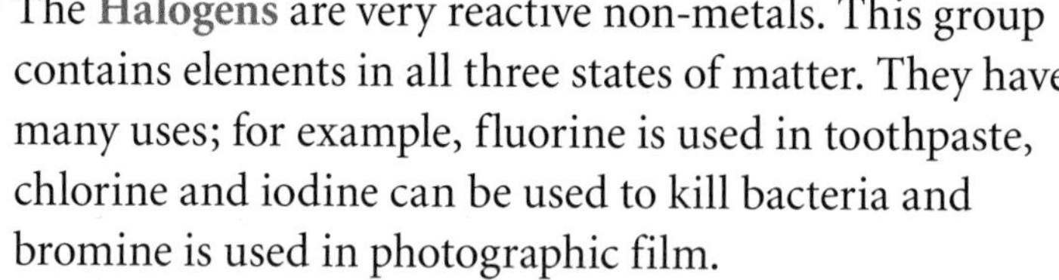

The **Halogens** are very reactive non-metals. This group contains elements in all three states of matter. They have many uses; for example, fluorine is used in toothpaste, chlorine and iodine can be used to kill bacteria and bromine is used in photographic film.

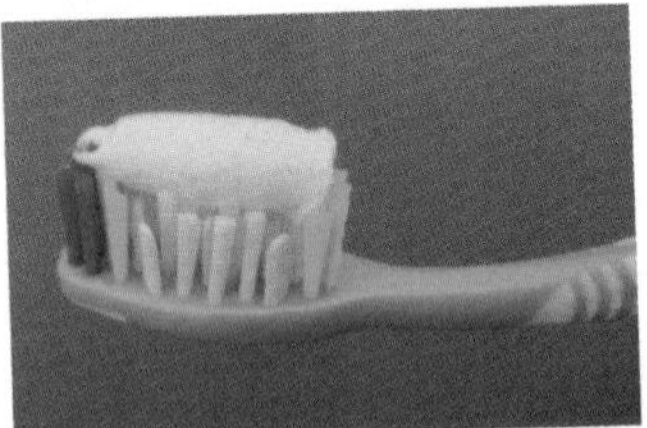

Noble Gases (Group 0)

The **Noble Gases** are very unreactive non-metals. Even although they are unreactive, they have many uses; from helium being used to fill balloons to their use in lighting.

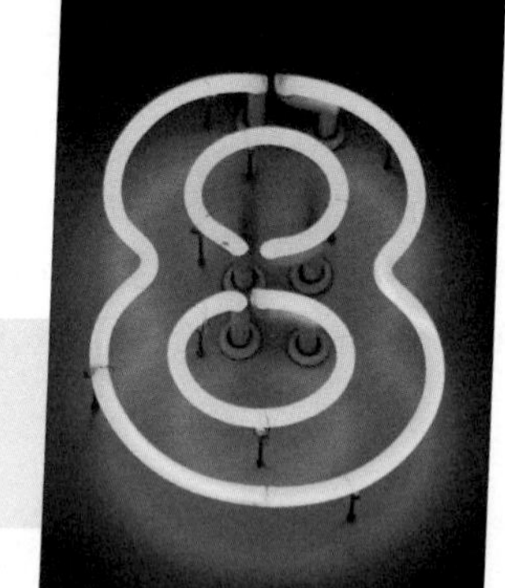

Neon signs like this are made from tubes that contain neon gas. The tubes are made of glass which has been carefully bent into shape.

In the middle of the Periodic Table we find the Transition Metals.

Transition Metals

The Transition Metals have many different properties and because of this they have many uses. For example, copper is used in wiring, iron is used in construction and platinum is used in catalytic converters in car exhausts.

The Clyde Arc (known locally as the Squinty Bridge) is a road bridge over the River Clyde in Glasgow. The arc is made of steel, which is mainly made of iron.

Active Learning

A new element has been discovered. Scientists have named the element 'Mandelium' after a famous South African politician. The properties of the new element are listed below.

Appearance: silvery and shiny.

Conductivity: conducts heat and electricity.

Reactions: very reactive with water.

a) Suggest a symbol for the new element.

b) In which Group of the Periodic Table should 'Mandelium' be placed?

c) Find out the name of the South African politician, and write a short passage about his life and works.

QUESTIONS

1 From the Periodic Table, pick an element which fits each of the descriptions below and give the element's symbol.

a) An element that is contained in compounds which are used to prevent tooth decay.

b) A gas that can be used in light bulbs.

c) A soft metal that is stored in oil because it is so reactive with water.

d) A metal that is used in the catalytic converter of car exhausts.

e) The first element in Group 0.

2 Give the name and number of the Group that each of the elements listed below belongs to.

a) sodium and lithium

b) chlorine and bromine

c) neon and argon.

The atom

John Dalton was an English chemist who became famous in the late 1700s for his work in the development of the nature of the atom. After performing many experiments he made some suggestions about atoms:

- Elements are made from tiny particles called atoms.
- All the atoms of one element are identical.
- The atoms of an element are different to the atoms of any other element.
- Atoms of one element can join with atoms of other elements to form compounds.

However, in the early 1900s, scientists proved that atoms are actually made up of even smaller **sub-atomic** particles called **protons, electrons** and **neutrons.**

Several scientists were involved in developing a theory as to how these particles were arranged in the atom. This Atomic Theory is outlined on the next page:

The atom

Atoms are made up of three smaller particles called:

Protons Positively charged particles which are contained in the **nucleus** of the atom (the centre). They have a mass of 1 a.m.u. (atomic mass unit). This is easier than listing the mass in grams which would be 0.00000000000000000000000167g.

Neutrons Neutrons are also contained in the nucleus of the atom but have no charge. A neutron weighs roughly the same as a proton, so it is also said to have a mass of 1 a.m.u.

Electrons Negatively charged particles that orbit around the positive centre of the atom in circles called energy levels. (Imagine how the moon orbits around the Earth.) Their mass is even smaller – it takes almost 2000 electrons to weigh the same as one proton or neutron, so they are considered to have zero mass.

This is summarised in the table below:

Particle	Mass	Charge	Location
Proton	1 a.m.u.	Positive	Nucleus
Neutron	1 a.m.u.	None (neutral)	Nucleus
Electron	0	Negative	Energy levels

Here is a diagram showing the make-up of an atom of helium:

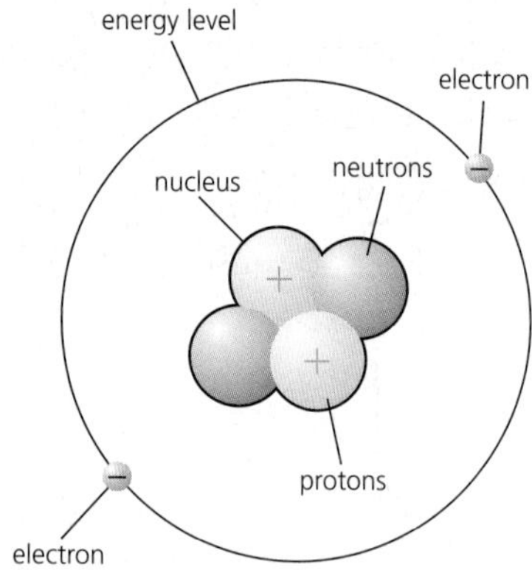

Although atoms contain negative electrons and positive protons, the atom overall is neutral (has no charge) because atoms contain equal numbers of protons and electrons, so they cancel each other out.

The **atomic number** of an element, which is given in the Periodic Table, is equal to the number of protons in each atom. For example, sodium has the atomic number 11. This means that an atom of sodium contains 11 protons and therefore 11 electrons.

QUESTIONS

1 Copy and complete the following statements.

Electrons carry a _________ charge.

Protons carry a _________ charge.

An atom consists of a nucleus which contains _________ and _________, surrounded by _________ .

Lithium has the atomic number of ___ and therefore its atoms have ___ protons and ___ electrons.

2 Atoms are described as being electrically neutral even although they contain positive particles called protons. Explain why atoms are neutral even although they contain these positive particles.

GLOSSARY

Alkali Metals the very reactive metals that are found in Group 1 of the Periodic Table

Atom a particle made up of protons, neutrons and electrons

Atomic mumber the number given to each element in the Periodic Table. It is equal to the number of protons in an atom

Compound a substance made up of two or more elements chemically combined

Density the mass of a substance in a given volume

Electron a negatively charged particle with zero mass found orbiting the nucleus of an atom in an energy level

Element contains only one type of atom

Halogens the reactive non-metals in Group 7 of the Periodic Table

Mixture two or more substances mixed but not chemically joined

Molecule two or more atoms held together by chemical bonds

Neutron a particle found in the nucleus of an atom with no charge and a mass of 1 a.m.u.

Noble Gases very unreactive non-metals found in Group 0 of the Periodic Table

Nucleus the positively charged centre of an atom that contains the protons and neutrons

Proton a particle found in the nucleus of an atom with a positive charge and a mass of 1 a.m.u.

MATERIALS

Properties and Uses of Substances

Pure as snow?

Level 2 What came before?

 **SCN 2-16a**

I have participated in practical activities to separate simple mixtures of substances and can relate my findings to my everyday experience.

Level 3 What is this chapter about?

 **SCN 3-16a**

I can differentiate between pure substances and mixtures in common use and can select appropriate physical methods for separating mixtures into their components.

Pure as snow?

Pure matter and mixed matter

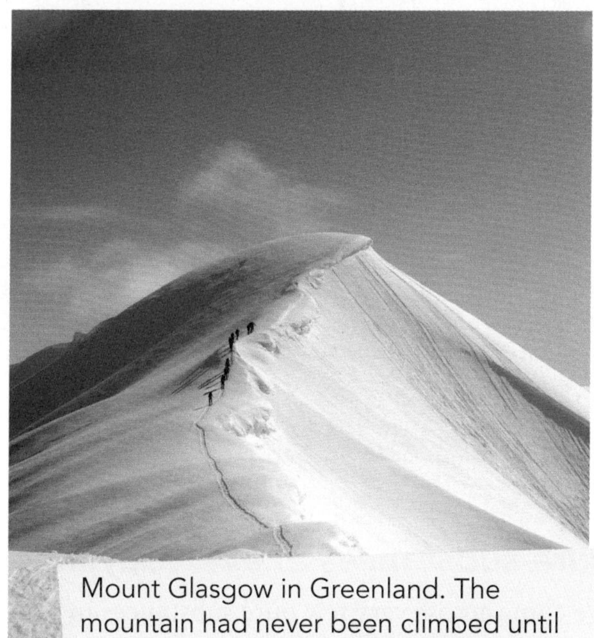

Mount Glasgow in Greenland. The mountain had never been climbed until a group of school pupils from Glasgow climbed it in July 2009. It had no name so they officially named it Mount Glasgow.

The snow on this mountain in Greenland is one of the purest substances there is, but the air around the mountain is a mixture.

What is a 'pure' substance?

Why do we use the word **pure**? We often say 'pure' when we mean 'clean', but pure things can be dirty and clean things are often not pure. In science, pure has a particular meaning. A pure substance is made of one single chemical, and nothing but that chemical. Most things we see and touch each day are not pure.

Honey

Silk from China

We hear people in adverts talk about 'pure honey' and see magazines advertising clothes made from 'pure silk', but to a scientist, honey and silk are not pure. Honey has got lots of things in it, including vitamin C, but it is mainly a **mixture** of glucose, fructose and water. Silk is a thread spun by a silkworm. It's not pure because it's made from more than one chemical; when people talk about pure silk, they mean material that is only made from silk thread and has no other type of man-made thread woven with it.

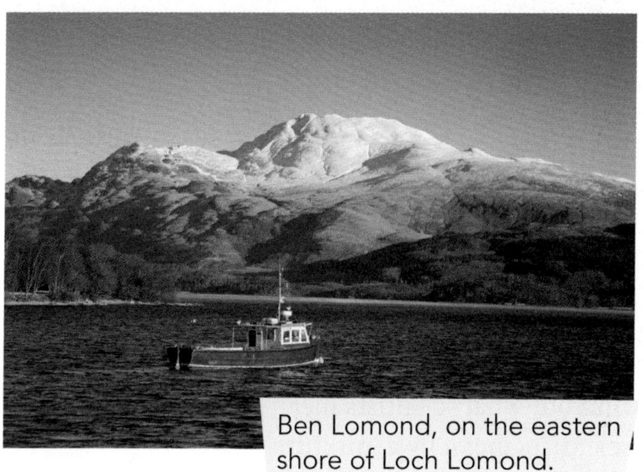

Ben Lomond, on the eastern shore of Loch Lomond.

If you stood on top of Ben Lomond in the rain, then the rain water would be almost pure as it fell through the air (there is a tiny bit of carbon dioxide dissolved in rain), but when it had flowed through the soil into a stream, it would not be pure any more. It would have dissolved some chemicals from the rocks and would have become a **solution**, so it would no longer be pure water.

How do we know if a substance is pure?

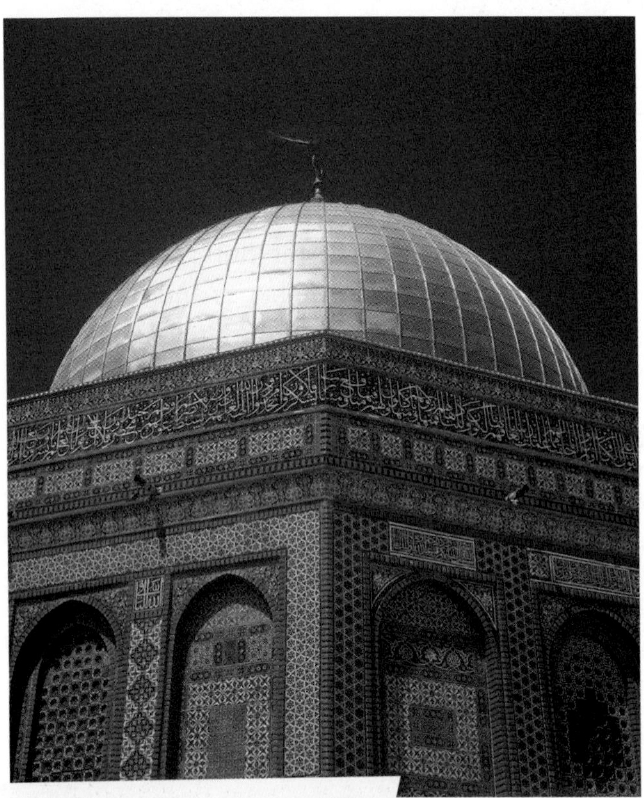

The gold on the dome of this mosque is a pure substance.

It is not always easy to know whether we are looking at a pure substance or a mixture. Before we can decide which is which, we will have to find out what scientists mean by 'pure' and what scientists mean by a 'mixture'.

In Chapter 2 you learned about elements and compounds. A pure substance is made from **only one element or only one compound** and is represented by a single chemical formula. If the pure substance is an element, then it only contains one type of atom, like gold, Au, only contains gold atoms. If the pure substance is a compound, it contains different types of atoms bonded together in fixed amounts. The compound called methane has the chemical formula CH_4. Methane is made from carbon and hydrogen atoms held together in CH_4 molecules. The **ratio** of carbon atoms to hydrogen atoms in methane is always 1 carbon atom to 4 hydrogen atoms. A pure compound cannot be broken down, without changing it into a new and different substance.

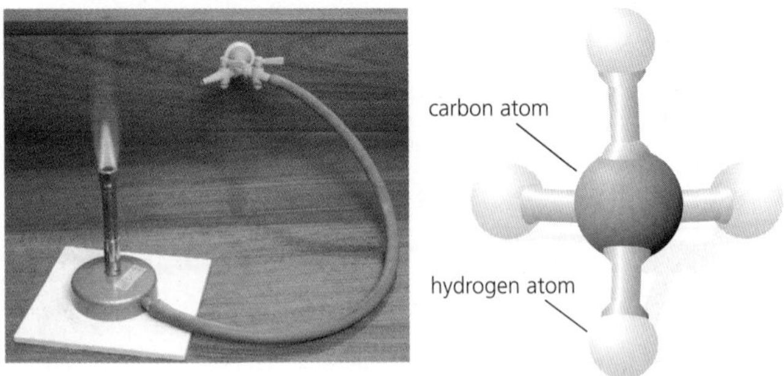

Pure substances in everyday life

We come across very few pure substances in everyday life. Just about all the things we eat and drink each day are mixtures. Pure water is hard to find, because water is a very good **solvent** so it tends to contain dissolved minerals and gases.

Some familiar substances that are pure are table salt (sodium chloride), white sugar, aluminium foil used in cooking and the copper used in electrical wiring.

Mixtures

Mixtures contain different elements or compounds that are physically mixed together but do not react chemically. The parts of a mixture can be present in any amount. If we have 1 g of salt mixed with a kilogram of sand and 1 g of sand mixed with a kilogram of salt, both are mixtures of salt and sand. The salt and sand do not combine to form new compounds, they only 'mix' together, but we can still identify them as salt and sand. This is the same for all mixtures so it should be quite easy to separate a mixture back into its original parts.

QUESTIONS

Fizzy drinks are often sold in cans. Explain whether you think a) the can and b) the juice are pure substances or mixtures.

Mixing matter

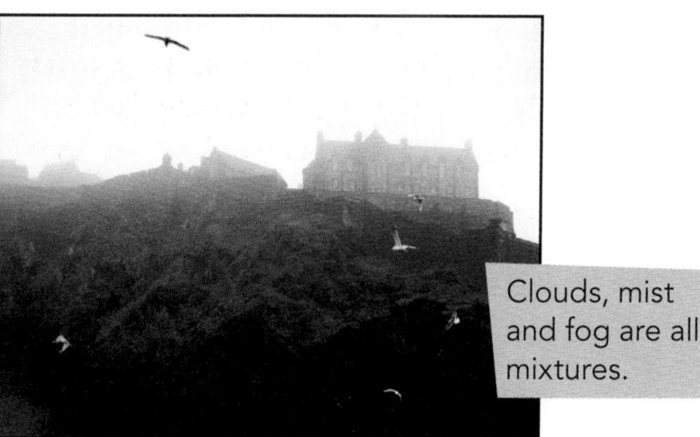

Clouds, mist and fog are all mixtures.

There are three states of matter and these can be mixed to give lots of familiar substances. These substances all look very different, but they have one thing in common, they are all mixtures. For instance, we can have mixtures of:

- solids in liquids, e.g. salt water or wet sand,
- liquids with liquids, e.g. milk or whisky,
- gases in liquids, e.g. fizzy drinks,
- gases with gases, e.g. air,
- solids with solids, e.g. concrete,
- solids in gases, e.g. smoke,
- liquids in gases, e.g. clouds, mist and fog.

In a solid/solid mixture, when one or both of the solids is a metal element, the mixture is given a special name; it is called an **alloy**.

QUESTIONS

Which types of matter are mixed in a cake a) before it goes in the oven and b) when it comes out of the oven?

Active Learning

Activity

When smoke is mixed with fog, we get smog. Until quite recently a lot of Scottish cities suffered badly from industrial smog. Write a newspaper article about the effect industrial smog had on people, why we used to get smog and why we do not get smog these days.

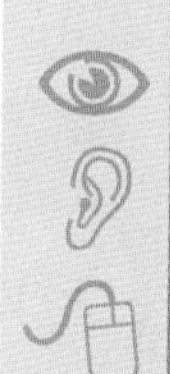

Particles and mixtures

Matter is all made from particles and some of these particles are bigger than others.

Scientists are interested in the size of the particles in a mixture because the size of the particles has an effect on the type of mixture we are looking at.

Atoms and molecules are far too small for us to see. If we put a spoonful of sugar in a glass of water and we stir the water, the sugar particles disappear. We know the sugar is still there, because the water tastes sweet, but we cannot see the sugar crystals any more. This is because the sugar molecules have moved out of the crystals and have mixed in with the water molecules. Both types of molecules are too small to be seen, and are too small to get in the way of light passing through the liquid, so this type of mixture looks clear; we say it is **transparent**. Mixtures like this are called solutions and any solid substance that seems to disappear when it's mixed with a liquid is said to be **soluble** in the liquid. A lot of substances are **insoluble** in water because their particles are held tightly to each other and cannot move away and mix with the water molecules.

If a mixture contains insoluble particles that are still small, but some of them are just big enough for us to see, the mixture is called a **suspension**. The insoluble particles are big enough to get in the way of light passing through the mixture so the liquid does not look clear, it is cloudy. Particles in a suspension are often big enough to sink to the bottom of the container so the particles in a suspension often do not stay properly mixed.

Fresh suspension of starch in water

after 10 minutes

after 30 minutes starch powder settles at the bottom of the beaker

QUESTIONS

1 Which of the words, solution or suspension, would best describe

a) a cup of black coffee

b) fresh orange juice?

2 Make a table with the headings 'solution' and 'suspension'. Fill in the table by writing the names of four liquids you think are solutions and four you think are suspensions.

Everyday mixtures

Just about everything we eat and drink each day is a mixture.

Cough mixture

Have you ever had a cough syrup? A lot of medicines given to children are suspensions. The medicine particles are mixed with syrup particles because the syrup hides the taste of the medicine. Suspensions have the largest particle size of any solid/liquid mixture and the solid particles can separate from the liquid and sink to the bottom of the bottle. If the instructions on a cough bottle say 'shake the bottle' then you know the mixture is a suspension and you have to shake it to make sure all the medicine particles are properly mixed with the liquid.

Glass

What do milk and glass have in common? They are both mixtures. Milk is a mixture of two liquids, whereas glass is a mixture of solids. Glass is mainly silica (silicon dioxide) with lime (calcium oxide) and some magnesium oxide and aluminium oxide added to make the glass less likely to be attacked by chemicals.

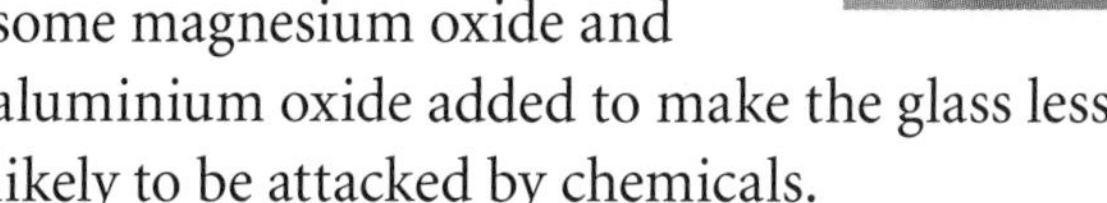

Mixtures can be 'customised' to make them more attractive or more useful. Mixing in some lead while glass is being made produces 'lead crystal', which sparkles more than normal glass. Adding some boron makes 'pyrex', which has a higher melting point and is harder to break than normal glass. Adding cobalt produces glass which has a wonderful deep blue colour.

Lead crystal

Cobalt glass

QUESTIONS

Pyrex and cobalt glass are both transparent. What does this tell us about the size of the particles in both mixtures?

Whisky

Whisky is transparent

Whisky contains lots of different chemicals, but the two main things mixed together in whisky are water and ethanol (ethanol is the chemical name for alcohol). Whisky is often coloured, but it is also clear (transparent), which means light can go straight through it. Molecules of ethanol mix easily with molecules of water so we say that ethanol is **soluble** in water. Both types of molecule, ethanol and water, are too small to have any effect on light as it travels through the mixture.

Fizzy juice

All fizzy juices contain a gas (carbon dioxide) mixed with a liquid (water). Fizzy juices are all clear so we know the gas has dissolved in the water. Carbon dioxide dissolves better in water if it is put under a bit of pressure. When you remove the top from a bottle, that pressure is released and you can see bubbles of gas forming in the liquid. Gases are lighter (less dense) than water so the bubbles all rise to the top and make a fizzing noise as they burst. The tiny bubbles get in the way of light passing through the juice so, for a short time, the mixture looks cloudy. When all the bubbles have burst, it goes clear again.

Everyday mixtures

Oddly enough, carbon dioxide is more soluble in cold water than in warm water so, if you like your juice very fizzy, it is best to keep it cool.

Alloys

Most of the metals we use each day are **alloys**. Alloys are a good example of very useful mixtures and are made by melting different metals (or metals and non-metals) and stirring them together. The atoms of the different metals are not chemically combined together, but the properties of the alloys are often very different from the properties of the separate metals. Solder is an alloy of tin and lead; solder can be used to join two pieces of metal and is often used to make electrical connections.

Steel, an alloy, was used to make the Forth Rail Bridge.

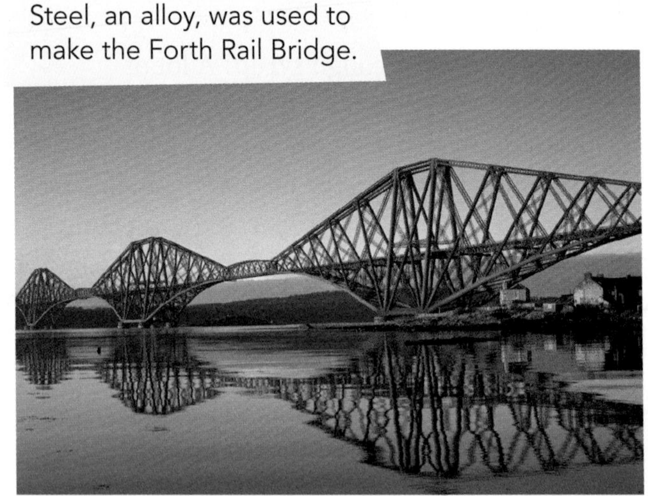

Practical

If we cut approximately 1 cm square of tin foil and a 0.5 cm square of lead foil we can estimate how hard each metal is by pressing the point of a sharp pencil in to each one. Bending the metals will show if they are **malleable**.

Your teacher will probably demonstrate the next experiments in a fume cupboard.

We can then put both pieces of metal foil in a pyrex ignition tube and, shaking the tube gently, heat it in a blue Bunsen flame. Once the metals have melted and mixed together, the tube can be left to cool. If the cool tube is turned upside down and tapped gently on a heating mat a small lump of the alloy (solder) will fall out.

If we test the alloy that has been made we can see that it is much harder than the two **component** metals. A further experiment would show that the alloy melts at a much lower temperature than either tin or lead. One way of doing this is to put a small piece of tin foil, a small piece of lead foil and the piece of solder at the points of a triangle on something like the lid of a coffee tin. The gauze is taken off a tripod and replaced by the lid, then the lid is heated from underneath by a Bunsen flame that is pointed at the centre of the triangle. We can then record the order in which the three samples melt.

Practical

Modern solder is usually a mixture of approximately 60% tin and 40% lead. Soldering is a very ancient technique (there is evidence that it was being used up to 5000 years ago) and alloys have been so important to mankind that we have named a historical age, the Bronze Age, after the alloy discovered at that time.

Soldering a copper pipe.

The most common alloy used in the world is steel. This is a mixture of iron and a non-metal, carbon. Iron is a metal that is not particularly hard, but when it is mixed with carbon, it makes the much harder alloy called steel. Steel is used to make cars and build bridges.

All our coins are alloys, because they need to be harder wearing than pure metals.

QUESTIONS

1 Which metals are mixed together to make bronze?

2 Why do you think new alloys are still being developed?

3 British 1p, 5p and £1 coins are made from different alloys. Find out which metals are used to make each of these three alloys. Why do you think three different alloys are used to make these coins?

4 Apart from being hard wearing, can you give another reason why our 'silver' and 'gold' coins are made from alloys?

5 Wood's metal is an alloy that is used as an easily melted plug in shop sprinkler systems. It contains bismuth (50%), lead (25%), cadmium (12.5%) and tin (12.5%). Draw a bar graph to show the composition of Wood's metal.

6 Find out the difference between 9 carat and 20 carat gold. Which of these would you prefer to have a ring made from? Explain your choice.

Active Learning

Use books or the Internet to find out when people started to use coins in Britain. Make a slide show on the history of Scottish coins and bank notes and present your show to the rest of the class.

Naturally occurring mixtures

Sea water

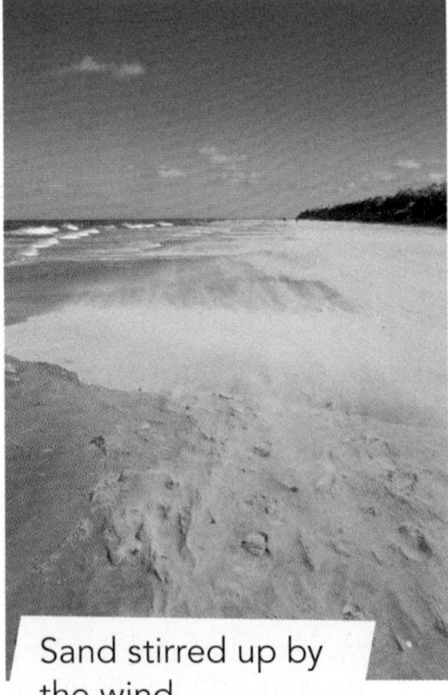
Sand stirred up by the wind.

Sea water contains a lot of different compounds, but the main one, the one we can taste when we are swimming, is common salt (sodium chloride). Sea water is a solution because the particles mixed with water are the size of molecules. On a calm, sunny day we can see all the living things in a rock pool, because the sea water is clear. On the day after a storm, the water at the edge of a sandy beach is often not clear. High winds stir up the sand so the sea water has particles of sand scattered through it; it has become a suspension, as well as a solution.

QUESTIONS

When sand and sea water are mixed in a bucket, the sea water looks cloudy. If the mixture is left undisturbed, overnight, the water becomes clear again. Why does this happen?

Air

Air is a mixture because it contains ten different gases: oxygen, nitrogen, carbon dioxide, water vapour and the six Noble Gases – helium, neon, argon, krypton, xenon and radon. The amount of water vapour in air changes according to the temperature of the air, but the amount of the other nine gases is fairly constant at sea level. Nitrogen makes up about 78% of the air. Oxygen is a gas needed by all living things and oxygen is also the gas that enables things to burn; we say oxygen 'supports combustion'. About one-fifth of the mixture of gases we call the atmosphere is oxygen. If more than one-fifth of the atmosphere was oxygen, the Fire Service would be very busy indeed!

QUESTIONS

1 Can you name another important gas, present high up in the atmosphere? There is only a small quantity of this gas, but it is needed to protect us from harmful UV radiation.

2 20% means the same as one-fifth. Express the following percentages as fractions.

a) 50% b) 25% c) 75% d) 10% e) 12.5%.

3 In groups, make a leaflet about the uses of the gases in the air. Include as many of the gases as you can and give the approximate percentage of each one in the atmosphere.

Crude oil

Crude oil is a fossil fuel found in the Earth's crust and is a black, sticky mixture of solids, liquids and gases. Almost all the compounds in crude oil are **hydrocarbons**, compounds which contain only carbon and hydrogen atoms. Crude oil is almost useless in its natural state; to make it useful crude oil has to be put through various processes which we call refining. You will find out more about crude oil and how it is separated to make useful substances in Chapter 8.

Crude oil

Properties of substances

You have already found out about the properties of some elements and compounds so you know that, in science, the word property means the way a substance looks or behaves, e.g. its colour, smell, melting or boiling point, solubility, electrical conduction, etc. A lot of the time, in science, we are trying to **separate** mixtures, to obtain pure substances, so it is important to know the properties of each of the substances in the mixture and then use these different properties to work out how to separate the mixture.

Getting pure substances from mixtures

All the common separation techniques we use in a lab are based on the fact that the chemicals in a mixture have different properties. All we have to do is to identify the properties and then make use of them.

Insoluble solids and liquids

After we have cooked pasta, we have to drain the water off. We can do this by holding the pan over the sink and tilting it, to pour the water away without losing any of the pasta.

This way of separating an insoluble solid from a liquid is called **decanting**. The problem with decanting is that it is slow and leaves quite a lot of water in with the pasta. A quicker, simpler method is to pour the mixture of pasta and water through a colander (or sieve).

Getting pure substances from mixtures

The pasta pieces are too big to go through the holes so they are separated from the water. This method of separating an insoluble solid from a liquid is called **filtration**. Decanting only works with quite big, insoluble particles because they sink to the bottom of the mixture and the liquid can be poured off. Filtration can be used to separate most insoluble solids from a liquid. In the lab, we use filter paper and filter funnels to separate mixtures.

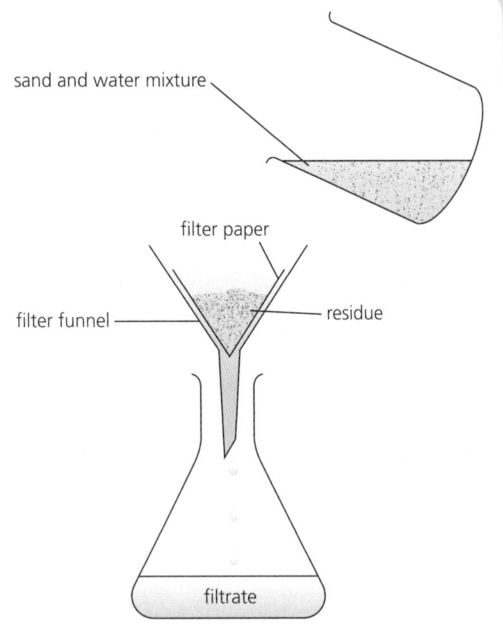

QUESTIONS

1. Can you think of anywhere else in the kitchen where filtration might be used?
2. Draw a scientific (cross-sectional diagram) of the filtration apparatus we could use to separate a mixture of grit and water. Label the residue and the filtrate.

Solutions

Salt pans in Lanzarote.

Getting a solid from a solution – evaporation

Copper sulphate is a blue solid that is soluble in water. To get solid copper sulphate from a solution, we heat the mixture until most of the water has **evaporated**, then stop heating and leave the liquid to evaporate slowly until copper sulphate **crystals** are formed.

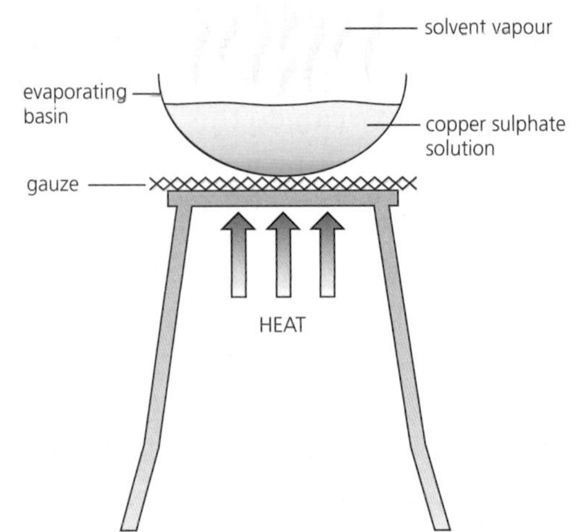

Solutions

Getting a liquid from a solution

If we want to recover pure water, for example, from a solution then we set up the apparatus shown here. When we heat the solution, water evaporates (changes from a liquid to a gas) and the gas moves through the apparatus. When it reaches the cooled **condenser** it condenses (changes from a gas to a liquid) and is collected.

This is known as a distillation apparatus. Distillation is normally used to separate mixtures of liquids. The liquid which is collected is called the **distillate**. In the example shown this is pure water.

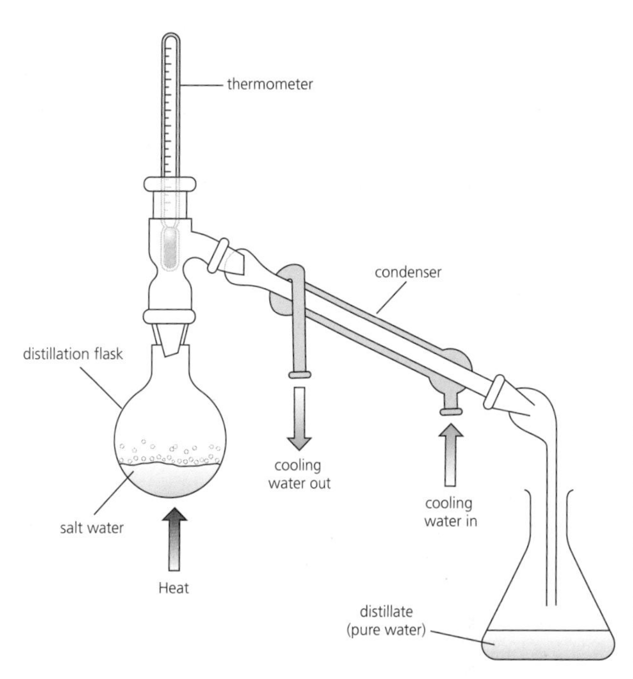

Liquid mixtures

Whisky

The whisky industry is very important to Scotland's economy and this industry depends on the separation of a liquid mixture. Barley and water are **fermented** to give a dilute solution (about 8%) of ethanol (alcohol) in water. This mixture is then separated by distillation. This is a simple process when we are separating a liquid from a solid as we did earlier in this Chapter, but when we are trying to separate a mixture of two liquids, it gets a bit more complicated. Basically, the mixture is heated and the liquid with the lower boiling point boils first. Ethanol boils at 79°C so it boils first. Water boils at 100°C, but even at 79°C, quite a lot of water evaporates along with the ethanol. The mixture of gases contains a higher percentage of ethanol than the original liquid mixture, but it not enough for us to call it whisky. The gas mixture is condensed and the liquid formed is evaporated again. That's what a whisky **still** does. It allows the process of evaporation followed by condensation to be repeated lots of times until the condensed liquid contains enough ethanol to be called whisky.

Liquid mixtures

Active Learning

Activity

1  In groups, research the importance of the whisky industry to Scotland. Find out how many Scottish distilleries there are, where in the country they can be found and how much money the industry makes each year. Why do people think Scottish whisky is the best in the world and how many other countries are also making whisky? Present your findings to the rest of the class in a poster or as a slide show.

2 Alcohol content is measured in units. A glass of wine or a measure of spirit contains one unit of alcohol, whereas a pint of beer, lager or a bottle of alcopop has two units. How many units of alcohol are there in:

a) three pints of lager

b) two glasses of wine and two measures of vodka

c) two bottles of alcopop and one measure of whisky?

3 Make an information leaflet that highlights the dangers of drink driving.

4 Use the Internet to try to find out how the gases shown opposite are extracted from the mixture of gases which we call air.

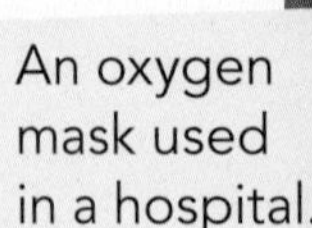

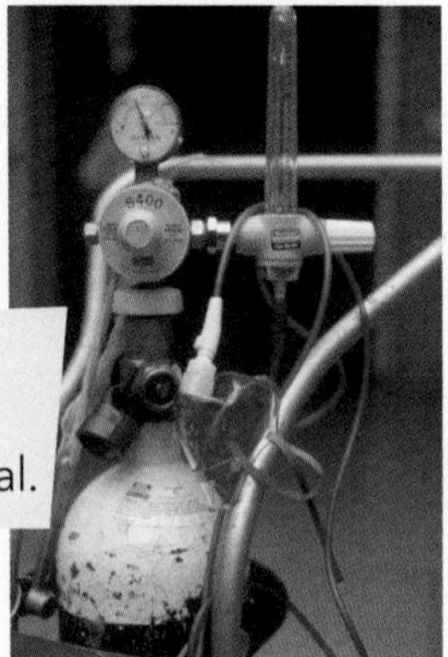

An oxygen mask used in a hospital.

Helium used to blow up party balloons.

An electric light bulb filled with argon.

Solid mixtures

Different solid mixtures are separated in different ways.

Iron filings are attracted to a magnet

Iron filings and sulphur powder

Iron is a heavy, black solid that sinks in water and is attracted to a magnet. Sulphur powder is a yellow solid that floats on water and is not attracted to a magnet.

One way of separating a mixture of iron filings and sulphur is to use a magnet.

QUESTIONS

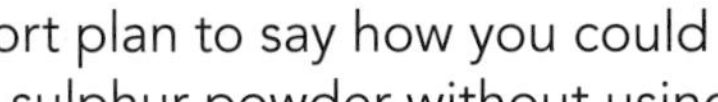

1 Write a short plan to say how you could separate a mixture of iron filings and sulphur powder without using a magnet.

2 Are all metals magnetic?

Iodine and salt

Iodine is a black, solid, non-metal element found in Group 7 of the Periodic Table. When iodine is heated gently, it sublimes; this means it changes from solid to gas without becoming liquid. Sodium chloride (table salt) is a white **crystalline** solid which has a high melting point and does not sublime. If we have a mixture of salt and iodine we can get pure salt by sitting with a magnifying glass and picking all the tiny black crystals of iodine out of the tiny white crystals of salt. Or we can use sublimation apparatus (often called a 'cold finger') to heat the mixture gently and let the sublimed iodine turn back into a solid on the cold surface.

QUESTIONS

Find out which gas in the air can form a solid that sublimes. At what temperature does this gas change into a solid?

Solid mixtures

Salt and sand

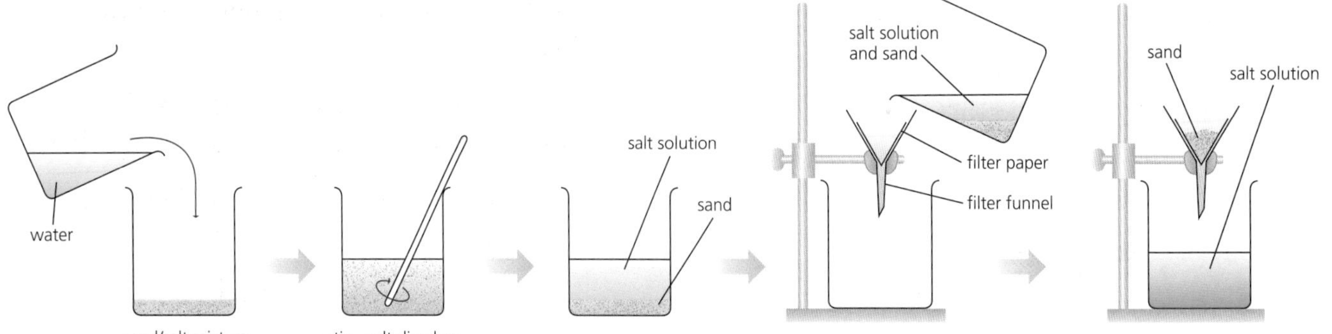

Active Learning

Activity

The diagrams above show part of the separation of salt and sand. Your task is to use the information from this section to write a paragraph describing, in detail, how you would get pure samples of sand and salt from a mixture. In your description you should use the words **soluble, insoluble, dissolve, filter** and **evaporation**.

QUESTIONS

Sugar is soluble in water and it is also soluble in alcohol. Salt is soluble in water, but it is not soluble in alcohol.

Describe how you could separate a mixture of sugar and salt to get pure samples of both salt and sugar.

Coloured mixtures

Food colourings, and the ink used in coloured pens, are usually mixtures. Coloured mixtures are separated by a technique called **chromatography**. A small drop of mixture is spotted onto absorbent paper, as shown here, and the bottom of the paper is placed in a solvent, usually water. The water moves up the paper and carries the coloured compounds with it. Some of the colours move faster than others so they are separated.

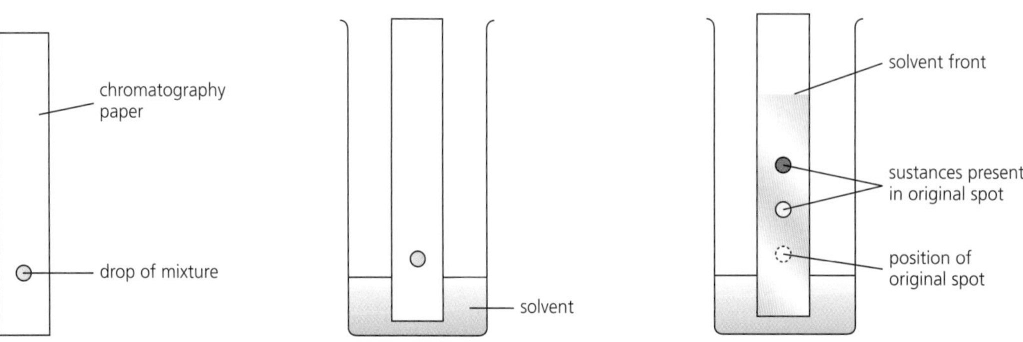

GLOSSARY

Alloy a mixture of a metal with another element, usually another metal

Compound a substance made up of two or more elements chemically joined

Crystalline something that has the structure of a crystal

Crystal a solid where the particles are arranged in a definite pattern

Decant to pour the liquid off, leaving the solid behind

Distillate a liquid obtained by the process of distillation

Element a substance that contains only one type of atom

Evaporate change from a liquid to a gas

Ferment the action of yeast on glucose, breaking it down to make ethanol and carbon dioxide

Hydrocarbon a compound containing only the elements hydrogen and carbon

Insoluble a substance that does not dissolve in a solvent

Malleable the ability to bend without breaking and to be beaten out into thin sheets

Mixture two or more substances mixed together, but not chemically joined together

Property an attribute that is always present in a particular compound or element

Pure made of only one chemical

Ratio the relation of one quantity to another

Separate to remove one part of a mixture from the other parts

Soluble a word used to describe a substance that dissolves in a solvent

Solute the substance that is dissolved in a solution

Solution the liquid formed when a solute has dissolved in a solvent

Solvent a liquid that can dissolve another substance

Suspension a mixture of a liquid with very small particles of an insoluble solid

Transparent Something that light can pass through

PLANET EARTH

Processes of the Planet

Earth matters

Level 2 What came before?

 **SCN 2-05a**

I can apply my knowledge of how water changes state to help me understand the processes involved in the water cycle in nature over time.

Level 3 What is this chapter about?

 **SCN 3-05a**

By contributing to experiments and investigations, I can develop my understanding of models of matter and can apply this to changes of state and the energy involved as they occur in nature.

Earth matters

Moving matter

Our beautiful planet is made of what scientists call matter. We can look at the matter around us and see mountains, rivers, oceans and clouds; these all look very different, but they all have one thing in common; they are made of very tiny, separate bits of matter called particles, and all those particles are in constant motion. The amount of movement and energy surrounding us is actually unbelievable. The newspapers and TV tell us there is an energy crisis on this planet yet the planet (and all the particles it's made from) have a huge amount of energy.

When you get out of bed in the morning you are surrounded by incredibly fast moving particles; you are being battered by air particles and each air particle is moving at about 500 metres per second (m/s) which is faster than the speed of sound. The floor you are standing on is made of particles; each particle stays in the same place but it is vibrating very rapidly. Our whole planet is in constant motion. It is spinning on its axis like a spinning top. At the equator the surface of the Earth is moving at roughly 460 m/s, or 1000 miles per hour, and, at the same time, our planet is circling the Sun at about 30 km/s, or 67 000 miles per hour. As well as all this, our solar system – the Earth, the Sun and all the other planets – is whirling around the centre of our galaxy at about 220 kilometres per second, or 490 000 miles per hour. These speeds are absolutely massive and it can make you quite breathless just thinking about it! How can we live on a planet that's moving so fast and feel as if we are standing still? Before we can start to understand the galaxy, we must first try to understand our planet. Scientists are people who try to find out about things and finding out about matter has told us quite a lot about how particles move around and how they can change from one state to another.

QUESTIONS

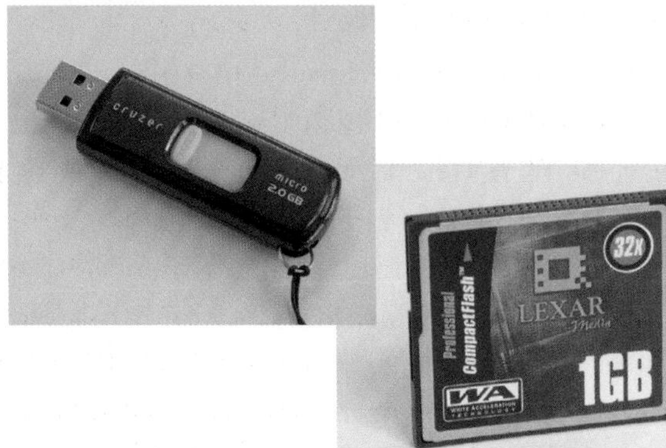

1 How many metres are there in 1 kilometre?

2 The number 1000 can be written as 1 × 103. Using this kind of notation, how would you write the numbers

a) 67 000

b) 490 000?

3 Some words begin with combinations of letters called **prefixes**; these are used to show how big or how small a measurement is. Use a book or the Internet to find out the meaning of these prefixes and find the symbol used to represent each of them. The first one has been done for you.

Prefix	Symbol	Multiplication factor
Tera	T	10^{12}
Giga		
Mega		
Kilo		
Deci		
Centi		
Milli		
Micro		
Nano		

Very small particles

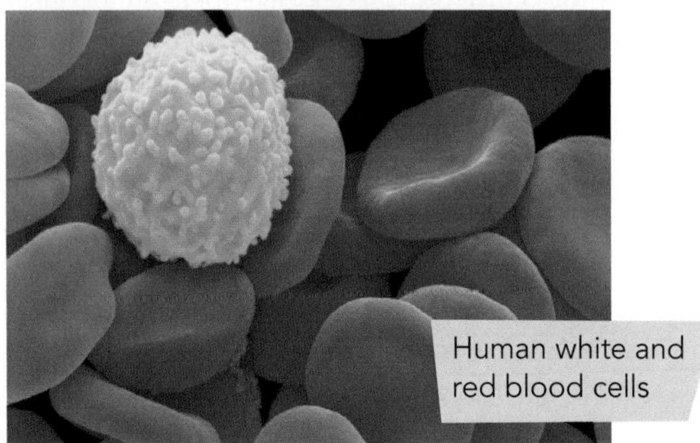

Human white and red blood cells

In this chapter, we are looking at particles in all three states of matter (solid, liquid and gas), but have you ever thought about the size of these particles? Air and water are made of very, very tiny particles called **atoms** and molecules. You learned what atoms and molecules are in Chapter 3 of this book; at the moment we are just thinking about their size.

Every cell in your body contains millions and millions of atoms and molecules, all taking part in the chemical reactions that keep you warm, keep you growing and keep you moving. It is really hard for us to imagine how small these particles are, but try this. A normal bag of white sugar weighs 1 kg. In that 1-kg bag, there are roughly 1 800 000 000 000 000 000 000 000 molecules of sugar. If all these (1.8×10^{24}) particles can fit into one bag of sugar, how incredibly tiny must they be?

To put it another way:

- 6.02×10^{23} kilograms is just over 20 times the mass of our planet, Earth.

Very small particles

- 6.02×10^{23} is the number of molecules in 18 ml (a small mouthful) of water.

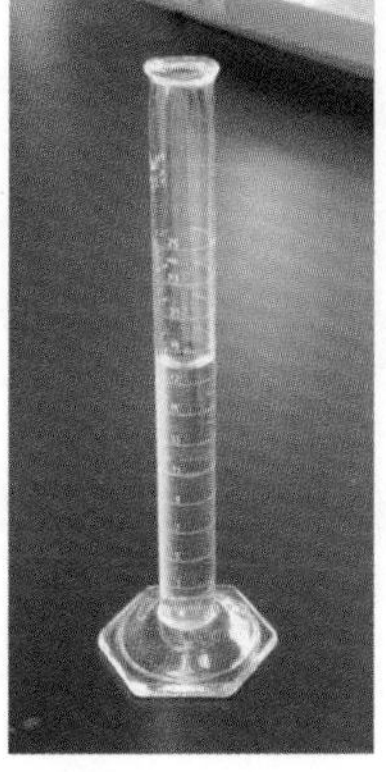

If you study chemistry later on in school, you'll find out why 6.02×10^{23} has been used here.

Even although they are so incredibly small, we have been able to 'see' atoms and molecules for the past 50 years, ever since scanning electron microscopes have been available. More recently, scientists have not only been able to see atoms, they have been able to actually move atoms around on the surface of a substance, and this has led to a boom in what is now called 'Nanotechnology'.

Nano is the Greek word for 'dwarf' and for many people, nano just means something that's smaller than the last version; for instance the iPod Nano is just a smaller version of the iPod Classic. In science and engineering, nano means something a bit more exact; it is a multiplication factor of 10^{-9}, which is one thousandth of a millionth.

As a length, a nanometre is a millionth of a millimetre. Look at a millimetre on your ruler and try to imagine dividing that little gap into a million smaller spaces; it's an amazing thought. One nanometre is about the length of five atoms joined together in a row and, using a very expensive piece of equipment called a scanning tunnelling microscope, we can do more than look at atoms. For the first time ever, scientists can change the way atoms are arranged on the surface of things and, because everything has a surface, nanotechnology is having an effect in just about every area of science.

We do have to remember, though, that what's called 'nanotechnology' is not a technology in its own right; it is just an 'enabling technology', or a tool, that allows something to be made, or done, differently, using less energy or using fewer raw materials. We also have to remember that nanotechnology is not new. Stained glass windows often contain red glass.

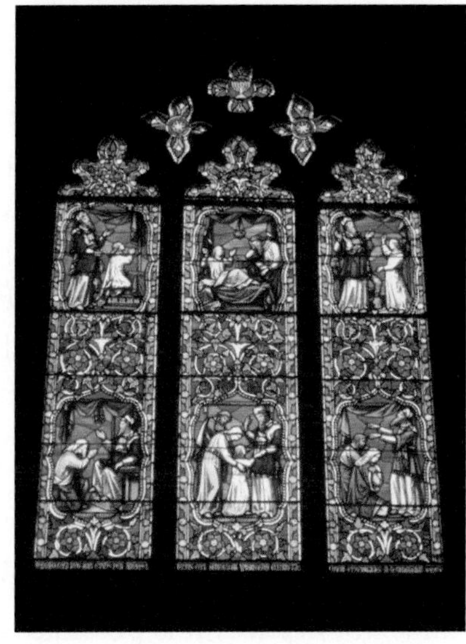

Medieval artists made red glass by mixing tiny particles of gold with molten glass; the gold particles were so small that these days they would be called nano particles. The British Museum has

Very small particles

a gold cloak that was found in North Wales. It is around 3500 years old and the gold has been beaten to the thickness of a sheet of paper.

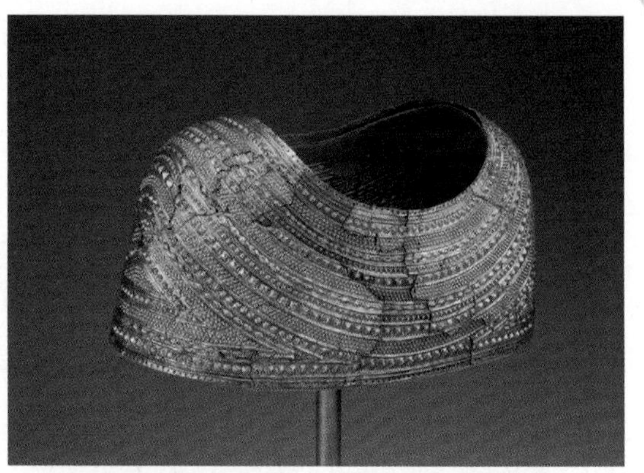

At the moment, mobile phone companies are funding research into very thin (nano scale) sheets of gold which could be used to make flexible phones that can be worn like bracelets. The difference between us and the medieval workers is that we have got a bit more knowledge and much better tools.

Does size matter?

In the past 100 years science has improved our quality of living to an unbelievable extent. We have mass-produced, cheap, warm clothes to wear, cars to drive, warm houses to live in, aeroplanes to take us on holiday and a massive choice of affordable food to eat. We are all consumers and consumers like things to be convenient, so our gadgets have got steadily smaller. In 20 years, the size of mobile phones has shrunk, while at the same time, they have become a lot more complex. We might think that nanotechnology is just part of this process of things getting smaller, but there is more to it than that.

Why nano is different

Nano science takes us to the end of the road for miniaturisation (things getting smaller) because it deals with some of the very smallest particles we know; atoms and molecules. Everything is made from them, so the possibilities to create new things could be endless. Now we have the tools that let us move atoms around we can look forward to huge improvements in medicines and in materials. Some hospitals are growing cartilage cells on a biodegradable nano scaffold; the cells are injected into a patient's knee and new cartilage grows, so an operation is not needed. It is possible to do the same with cells that grow new bone; breaks could mend faster using this technique, but what if an athlete wanted to strengthen his/her bones, perhaps to increase endurance? Should a technique developed to mend damaged bone be used to strengthen healthy bone? Would that be cheating?

Nano particles of the element silver (Ag) kill bacteria. Socks containing silver nano particles would not smell, no matter how hot your feet got. Producing these socks seems a great idea, but there is a problem. Some water treatment plants use bacteria as part of the process of cleaning waste water so when these socks are washed, silver nano particles could be released into the water and they might kill the useful bacteria.

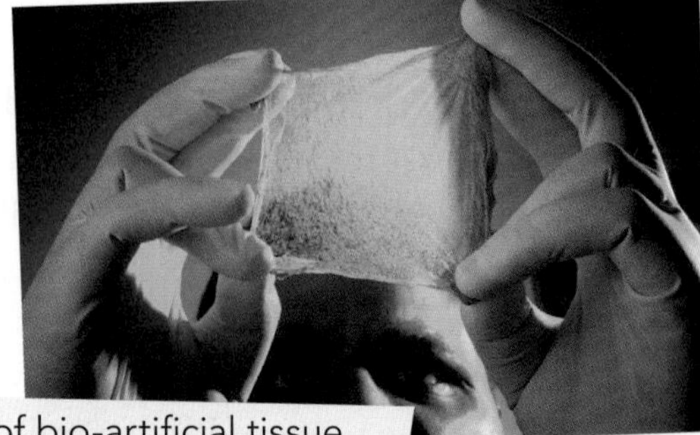

A sample of bio-artificial tissue created by 'printing' a mixture of living cells and viscous polymer into a tissue scaffold.

Why nano is different

A lot of money is being spent on trying to use nanotechnology to produce computers the size of a grain of sand, or smaller. These tiny processors will let us do lots of things, from speeding up medical diagnosis by building 'lab-on-a-chip' devices which are easily portable, need only tiny amounts of a sample and give a diagnosis almost instantaneously, to being used in food packaging to monitor bacteria levels and lengthen shelf-life. Tiny computers will bring us huge advantages, as long as we devote as much time and thought to their disposal as we do to their development.

Nanotechnology is bringing us fascinating and exciting new ideas and developments and we all need to keep ourselves informed about them, so we can all benefit from the advantages and avoid any possible problems.

Active Learning

Activity

On YouTube, watch 'The strange new world of nanoscience', narrated by Stephen Fry.

Explore the website www.nanoyou.eu. Try to find out:

- three uses of nanotechnology;
- the properties of Nano-tex, a new fabric designed using nanotechnology, and which natural material this fabric is modelled on;
- why scientists are keen to develop more uses of nanotechnology; and
- the concerns some scientists have about nanotechnolgy.

States of matter

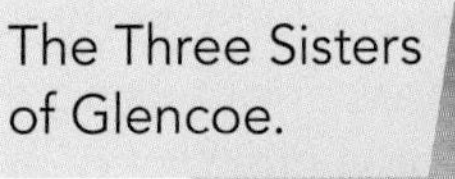
The Three Sisters of Glencoe.

You already know that heating solid water (ice) turns it into liquid water and heating liquid water changes it into a gas called water vapour. Water on the Earth can change state as it moves round the planet. The sun shines and the heat makes liquid water from the oceans **evaporate** and form water vapour. The vapour rises into the atmosphere; it cools, **condenses** and makes clouds, which are tiny droplets of liquid water floating in the air. The clouds move north, get very cold and the water **freezes** before falling as snow. Together these processes are known as the **water cycle**. The water cycle shows that a substance can change state if it is heated or cooled.

Changes of state

Most of the stuff on our planet will change its state if it is heated enough or cooled enough. The particles in water vapour (a gas) are just the same as they are in water (a liquid); it is just that the gas particles have more energy and are moving faster. When a gas condenses, or a liquid solidifies, the particles lose energy and slow down. Water is not the only stuff on the planet that is present in different states. We know that the Forth Rail

Changes of state

Bridge is made of solid iron, but the **core** of the Earth is mainly melted iron (a very hot liquid). Edinburgh Castle stands on solid rock, but the Earth's **mantle** is made of flowing streams of **molten** rock (see also Chapter 7).

If you look around the room you are in, most of the things you see are solids, but what about the matter you cannot see? We cannot see air so we often forget it is there, but we could not live without it. If it is cooled a lot and pressurised (squeezed) a bit, air changes from a gas to a liquid. When air is liquid, it can be distilled and all the ten gases in the air can be separated; that is how we get helium for party balloons.

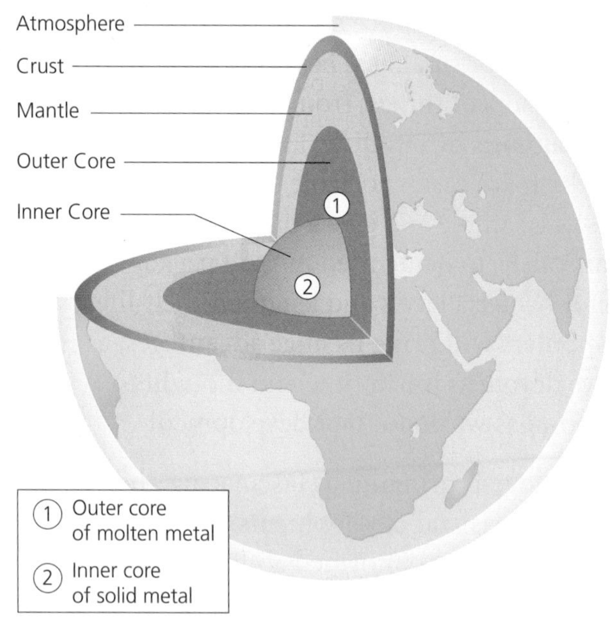

QUESTIONS

1 What do you think the word 'molten' means? Write down what you think it means then check you are correct using either a dictionary in a book, or a dictionary online.

2 All changes of state are described by a particular word. Copy out the table below and fill in the gaps.

Change of state	Describing word
solid to a liquid	
	evaporating
	freezing (or solidifying)
gas to a liquid	
	subliming

3 Which changes of state are involved in each of these processes?

a) glaciers forming

b) icebergs melting

c) windows steaming up on a cold morning

d) a kettle boiling.

4 When a dog is too hot, it lets its tongue hang out of its mouth and it breathes very fast. How do you think this helps it to cool down? When you are too hot, how does your body cool itself down?

5 Icebergs float in the sea. What does this tell you about the **density** of ice compared with the density of water?

Experiments

If we want to find out more about the matter the planet is made from, we have to do some experiments and make some **observations**.

Solids

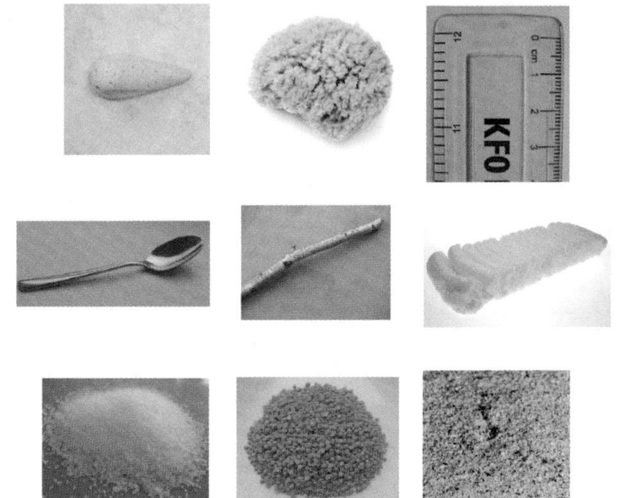

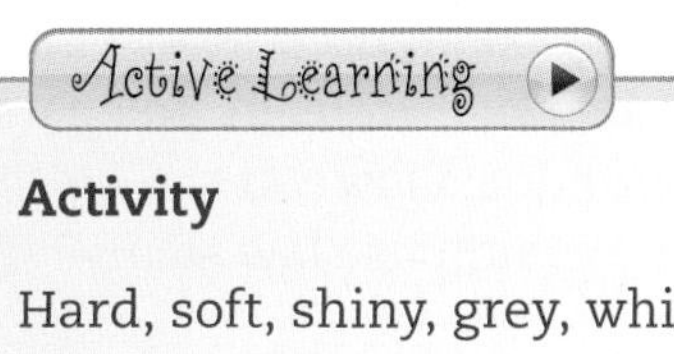

Active Learning

Activity

Hard, soft, shiny, grey, white, heavy.

Use the words in this list to help you describe each of the solids shown on the left. Do all the solids look like solids? Can any of them flow like a liquid does? What is the difference between the solids that 'flow' and the solids that do not?

Your teacher may show you a display of different solids which includes a sponge, a pumice stone, a plastic ruler, a metal spoon, a piece of wood, cotton wool, table salt, lentils and sand. Some solids have air trapped inside them. Use a magnifying glass to look carefully at the spaces in the sponge, and in the piece of pumice stone. What do you think is in the spaces? Put the sponge in water and squeeze. What is inside the bubbles which appear?

Liquids

Put some food dye in water and measure 50 ml of the coloured water into a measuring cylinder. Pour the water from the cylinder into a conical flask and then into a beaker. What do we mean when we say a liquid has a fixed **volume**? Explain why you think it is correct to say that liquids have a fixed volume but no fixed shape.

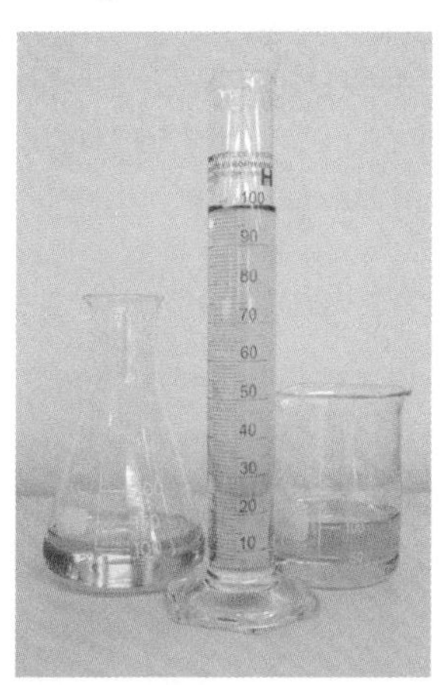

Liquids other than water

Look at some different liquids. This display includes glycerol, cooking oil and nail varnish remover. Can you name any other liquids that are not water and are not solutions made by dissolving substances in water?

Experiments

Activity

Thick, colourless, viscous, runny.

Viscous means how thick a liquid is. A viscous liquid does not flow easily. Use the words in this list to help you describe each of the liquids shown at the bottom of the previous page. Do all the liquids flow easily?

Investigation

If we have a white tile, dropping pipettes and a selection of liquids such as syrup, tomato sauce and water, we can find out which liquid is the most **viscous** and which is the least viscous.

What measurements would you have to make?

Is there another piece of equipment you would need that is not in the list of apparatus?

What do you think would happen to the viscosity of all the liquids if they were cooled in the fridge?

Gases

Your teacher will spray some perfume at one side of the room. Why can you smell the perfume at the other end of the room so quickly?

You can only smell a thing if particles of the substance go up your nose, so we need to find out how particles of the spray move across the room so quickly.

Perfume spray

Some facts about gases

Air is a mixture of gases. The particles of these gases are very tiny. They are very far apart from each other and they move very fast. Because air particles move so fast, they collide with the perfume particles, and the perfume particles pick up energy as they bounce off the air particles. It is hard to believe, but an average air particle collides with another air particle five times every nanosecond (one nanosecond is 1×10^{-9} seconds; this is such a tiny time interval that it is hard to imagine). The perfume particles move across the room very slowly, compared with the speed of the air particles, because they follow a zig-zag path as they are **bombarded** by air particles. When one set of particles moves through another set of particles, such as perfume through air, we call the process **diffusion**.

The kinetic theory of matter

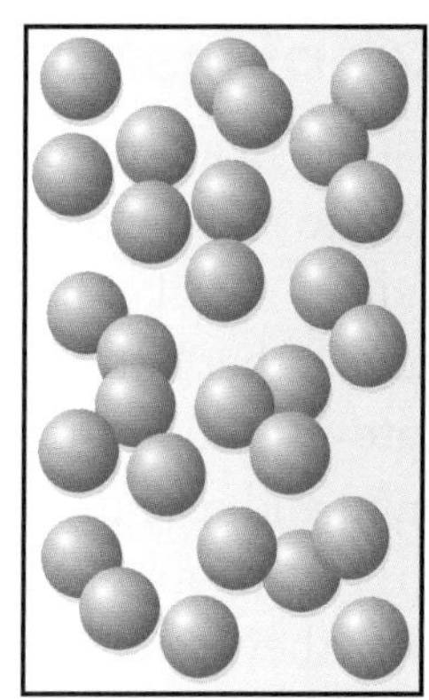
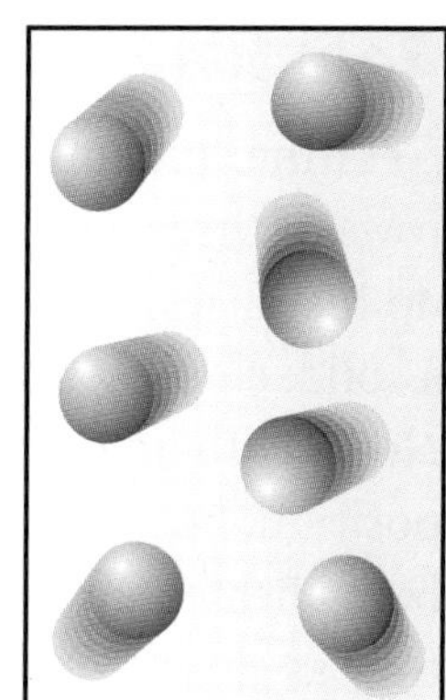

The idea of a theory might sound complicated, but the word **kinetic** means 'moving' and the kinetic theory of matter says that all matter is made of particles and those particles are constantly moving. In a solid, the particles are packed very close together; they are fixed in one position, but they can still vibrate. In a liquid, the particles are a little bit further apart and they can move past each other (we say they can **flow**). In a gas, the particles are very far apart and move very fast in all directions. All particles are attracted to each other. The particles in a solid are attracted to each other very strongly, the particles in a liquid are attracted to each other quite strongly and the particles in a gas are only very slightly attracted to each other. A substance does not always have to be in the same state. If the temperature or pressure changes, then the state of the substance can change as well.

QUESTIONS

Here are some mixed up bits of sentences about the particles in solids, liquids and gases. Think about them, discuss them and then put them into three groups: a group that can be used to describe solids, a group that describes liquids and a group that describes gases.

Once you have sorted them out, put each group of facts together and use the information to make a complete sentence about each of the three states of matter.

Use the glossary at the end of this chapter to find the meaning of any word you are not sure about.

1. the particles are very far apart
2. the substance does not flow
3. the substance cannot be **compressed**
4. the substance has a very low density
5. the substance has a fixed shape
6. the substance can flow
7. particles are close together, but can move past each other
8. the substance has no fixed volume
9. the substance has a fixed shape
10. the substance has a fixed volume
11. the particles are packed very close together
12. the substance does not have a fixed shape
13. the substance can be compressed

Practical

Role play: states of matter

Get nine students to stand in a square, in three rows of three. Get them to stand close together and do toe raises. The students are like the particles in a solid, closely packed together but still moving. Now get them to **rotate** – stand in the same position, but spin round and round. The solid is being heated up and is getting more energy. Are they as close together as they were before? Now get them all to try to move into another person's position inside the imaginary square. The solid is melting. Finally, get the nine students to run around in the square, they will spill out of the space because they need a lot more room to move around; they have evaporated and are now particles in a gas.

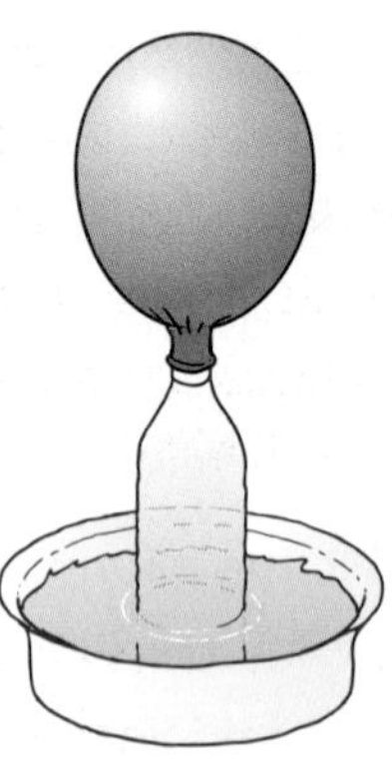

Read the introduction to each of the following activities. Do (or watch your teacher demonstrate) the experiment, then write a short description of **what** happens and a short explanation of **why** it happens. Check the end of this section to see if you were right.

- Stretch the mouth of a balloon over the top of an empty, plastic bottle. Hold the bottle in a bowl of hot of water for 3 or 4 minutes then take it out and let it cool down.
- Put three heaped teaspoons of bicarbonate of soda into a balloon. One-third fill a plastic bottle with vinegar. Stretch the mouth of the balloon over the top of the bottle, without letting any solid fall into the bottle. When the balloon is fitted over the bottle, hold the balloon upright and shake the solid into the vinegar.
- Put one quarter of an effervescent vitamin C tablet in the lid of a film canister (attach it with blue tack) then half fill the canister with water. Push the lid on firmly, turn the canister upside down and stand back. It is a good idea to put the inverted canister on a tray or something similar to reduce the mess.

Further activities

- Repeat the last experiment but this time put a thin cardboard tube over one of the canisters. Add a nose cone and fins to make a space rocket. Find out if the design can be changed to produce a rocket that travels further than the rest.
- Drop currants into fresh, fizzy lemonade. Why do the solid currants 'dance' up and down in the liquid? What can you see on the surface of the currants?
- Weigh a balloon which has not been blown up, then blow it up and weigh it again. The balloon is big but why is it not heavy?
- Weigh a sealed bottle or can of fizzy juice. Take the top off (be careful that it does not lose any liquid by fizzing over), leave it open until the end of the lesson and weigh it again. Alternatively, the can/bottle could be left on a digital balance and its change in mass recorded by looking at the reading every 15 minutes.

Further activities

- Put a spatula of solid copper carbonate into a pyrex tube and heat the tube in a blue Bunsen flame until all the solid changes colour. Watch the solid carefully and write down all the changes you see. Do you think the solid changed state when you heated it?

Explanation of each experiment

- The balloon starts to inflate because the bottle is full of air. As the air particles are heated up, they get more energy so they move faster. When they move faster, they take up more space; we say the gas expands and gets lighter (less dense) so the gas rises up into the balloon and the balloon starts to inflate.

  When the bottle is taken out of the water, it cools down and the particles lose energy so they start to slow down. As they move more slowly, they need less space to move in (we say the gas contracts).

- Vinegar reacts with bicarbonate of soda to make a gas called carbon dioxide. The particles in a gas are a lot further apart than the particles in a liquid or solid, so a gas needs to have a lot more space than a liquid or a solid. The gas that is made in this reaction pushes against the sides of the balloon and blows it up.
- The particles in a gas are a lot further apart than the particles in a liquid or solid, so gases are much lighter than liquids. When the solid and liquid react, the gas that is made pushes up through the liquid and breaks out of the surface, making the liquid froth and fizz. Once the gas has escaped from the surface, it spreads out. If the gas is trapped inside a small container it cannot spread out, so pressure builds up until the lid of the canister blows off.
- Bubbles of gas form on the surface of the dried fruit and, because the gas is very light, the bubbles lift the currants to the surface. At the surface of the liquid, the bubbles burst, the gas escapes into the air and the currants fall back to the bottom.
- A very small amount of gas takes up a big space because gas particles hardly attract each other at all; because gas particles are very far apart, a very small number of particles do not weigh much, but they take up a lot of space.
- It will get lighter as the carbon dioxide gas, which makes it fizzy, escapes into the air. Oddly enough, carbon dioxide gets more soluble as the water gets colder so more carbon dioxide dissolves in cold liquids than in warm liquids; this means that chilled lemonade is fizzier than warm lemonade.
- When copper carbonate is heated, it **decomposes** to leave a black solid (called copper oxide) and gives off a gas called carbon dioxide. When the green powder is changing to a black powder, it looks as if it is a liquid because the powder particles 'pop' open as the gas is released. The gas escaping from the powder makes the solid move around in the way that a liquid would.

Put enough stearic acid into a pyrex test tube to cover the bulb of a thermometer. Warm the tube gently to melt the solid. Put the thermometer into the liquid and record the temperature every 10 seconds as it cools. Plot your results on a graph with time on the horizontal axis and temperature on the vertical axis.

Heating solid stearic acid

The graph below shows the way the temperature of some stearic acid changes as it is heated until it becomes a liquid and then a gas. The graph is made up of five different sections labelled A, B, C, D and E. For each section, choose the sentence which describes what is happening at that stage from the coloured boxes around the graph. In your jotter, make a copy of the graph and beneath it write the letters A to E beside the correct sentence.

As the solid changes to a liquid, the temperature does not rise because all the energy is being used to overcome the strong forces of attraction between the particles and to separate them.

The temperature rises as the particles move around faster.

The particles move around faster as they gain energy so the temperature rises.

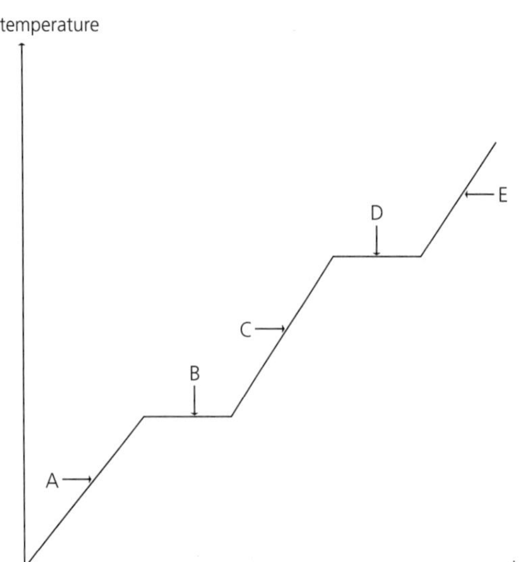

As the particles in the solid gain heat energy they are vibrating more and more, so the temperature rises.

The heat energy is all being used to separate the particles and overcome the forces of attraction between them so the temperature does not rise as the liquid changes to a gas.

Particles moving in liquids

Teacher demonstration

Place a petri dish on a white tile or piece of white paper or on an overhead projector. Fill it nearly to the top with pure water. Using tweezers, place a crystal of lead nitrate at one side of the petri dish and a crystal of potassium iodide at the other. Watch as the crystals begin to dissolve and a new compound is formed between them. Lead nitrate and potassium iodide are colourless, soluble compounds that react together to make a yellow, insoluble solid called lead iodide. You can see a line of lead iodide forming in the petri dish. The only way this could happen is if particles of the two colourless compounds move (diffuse) through the particles of liquid, meet together and react. The yellow line forms closer to the lead nitrate crystal than to the potassium iodide crystal because lead particles are bigger and heavier than iodide particles so they move (diffuse) more slowly.

GLOSSARY

Bombard to batter something with a lot of high speed particles

Compress to make something smaller by squeezing (pressurising) it: gases can be compressed because there are big spaces between particles; liquids and solids cannot be compressed

Condense change from a gas to a liquid

Core central part of the Earth, made mainly of molten iron

Density describes how closely particles are packed together

Evaporate change from a liquid to a gas

Freeze change from a liquid to a solid

Mantle layer of molten rock around the Earth's core

Molten a word describing a liquid formed by heating a solid

Sublime change from a solid directly to a gas

Viscous thick and sticky; does not flow well; difficult to stir

Volume the space a substance occupies

Water cycle the movement of water around planet Earth as a liquid, a gas and a solid

MATERIALS

Properties and Uses of Substances

6

Hide and seek!

Level 2 What came before?

 **SCN 2-16b**

By investigating common conditions that increase the amount of substance that will dissolve or the speed of dissolving, I can relate my findings to the world around me.

Level 3 What is this chapter about?

 **SCN 3-16b**

I have taken part in practical investigations into solubility using different solvents and can apply what I have learned to solve everyday practical problems.

Hide and seek!

What is a solution?

Most liquids that we drink are mixtures called **solutions.** Even tap water is a solution. Most solutions that we come across are a mixture of water and other chemicals. One of the chemicals dissolved in tap water is chlorine. Chlorine is added to water to kill germs.

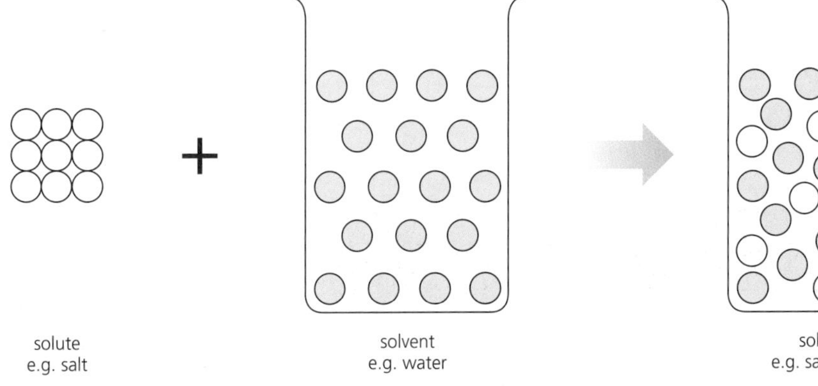

When a solute dissolves its particles mix in with the solvent particles.

The liquid that the chemicals dissolve in is known as the **solvent. Solute** is the name given to any substance (solid, liquid or gas) that dissolves in the solvent. The mixture which is formed when the solute dissolves in a solvent is called a solution. It looks as though the solute 'disappears' when it dissolves but what is really happening is that its particles are mixing in with the solvent particles – it's a bit like a game of hide and seek.

Substances which can dissolve in a liquid are said to be **soluble**. Sugar and salt are both soluble in water – they dissolve in water. Substances which cannot dissolve are **insoluble**. Sand is insoluble in water, which is why the sea cannot wash away the sand on a beach!

Dissolving a solute, like dissolving sugar in a cup of tea, is an example of a **physical change**. You are not making a new chemical substance. You are just mixing chemicals together.

Concentrated or dilute?

A **concentrated solution** has a large mass of solute dissolved in it. For example, diluting juice has lots of sugars and other chemicals dissolved in it. This is why it has a strong taste! A **dilute solution** has a much smaller mass of solute dissolved in it. You can make a dilute solution by simply adding more water to a concentrated solution.

a concentrated solution

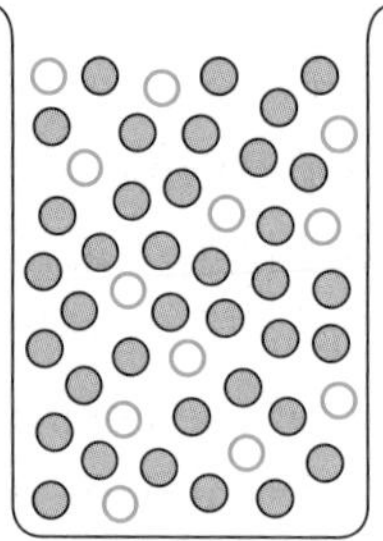

lots of diluting juice particles (●) in a small volume of water (○)

a dilute solution

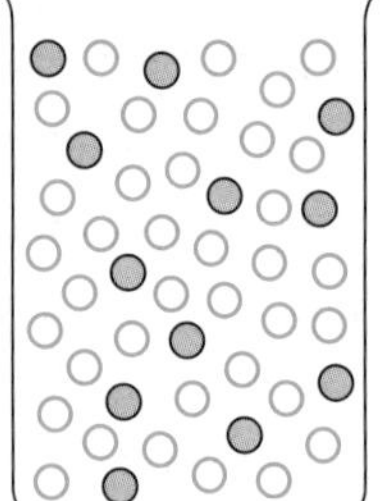

only a small number of diluting juice particles (●) in a large volume of water (○)

Speed it up!

When you add a spoonful of sugar to a cup of tea, why do you stir it? The sugar would eventually dissolve in the tea anyway, but stirring makes it dissolve faster. You can speed up dissolving in lots of ways – you can increase the temperature of the solvent, stir the mixture, crush the solute up into smaller pieces, use more solvent and less solute.

QUESTIONS

1 Tap water and mineral water are both solutions. In each case the solvent is water. Use the Internet and look on the label of a bottle of water to find the names of solutes that can be found in both tap and mineral water.

2 Use a bar chart or a table to present your findings from question 1 in a different way.

3 Look at the label on the bottle of cola shown here.

Name the solutes, the solvent and the solution.

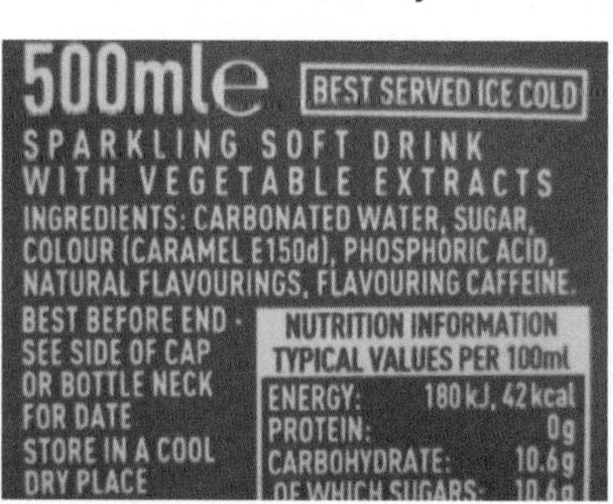

4 Sahid made a solution by dissolving coffee powder in a cup of hot water. Sahid says that making a cup of coffee is an example of a physical change because he could get the spoonful of coffee back if he wanted it. Describe an experiment that Sahid could do to prove that it is a physical change.

5 Describe an experiment that Sasha could do to explore how to speed up dissolving a sugar cube in a cup of hot water.

6 Use a temperature probe or thermometer to find out whether dissolving is an **exothermic** or **endothermic** process.

We all need solutions

Tap water

Tap water and mineral water are solutions, made of a mixture of water and solutes. Water has oxygen gas and minerals dissolved in it. Tap water has other solutes added to it. Sodium fluoride is a solute that is added to tap water in England to protect against tooth decay. As mentioned earlier chlorine is also added to tap water to kill germs. To make 'pure water' all the solutes have to be removed from the water using a process called distillation (see Chapter 4). Distilled water is used by scientists in certain chemistry and biochemistry experiments. It is also used to top up lead/acid batteries in cars, in steam irons and in antifreeze. This is because removing the minerals from the water prolongs the life of the machinery.

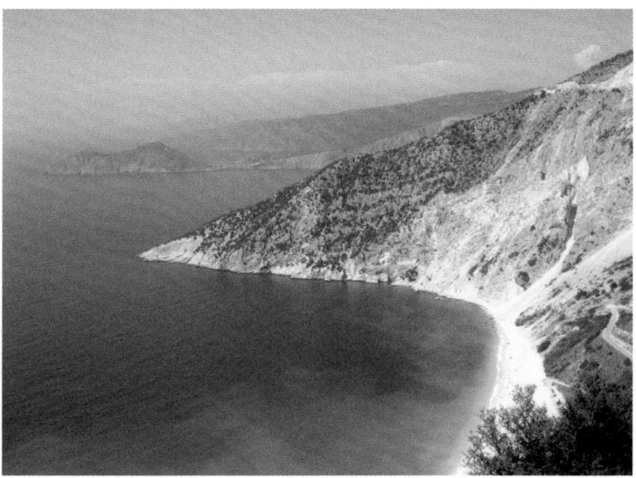

Sea water

Sea water is another common solution. You only need to get it in your eyes or to taste it to realise that there is salt dissolved in it. Lots of salts are dissolved in sea water including table salt, sodium chloride. You will also find magnesium sulphate, potassium bromide and several other salts.

Blood

Blood is an essential solution. The solvent in blood is water but what are the solutes dissolved in it? Most of the solutes in blood are proteins, for example, the protein called Factor XIII which is missing from the blood of haemophiliacs. The blood of haemophiliacs takes longer to clot which means that they bleed for a long time after they cut themselves. Other solutes in blood include sugars, fatty acids and amino acids, salts and **hormones**.

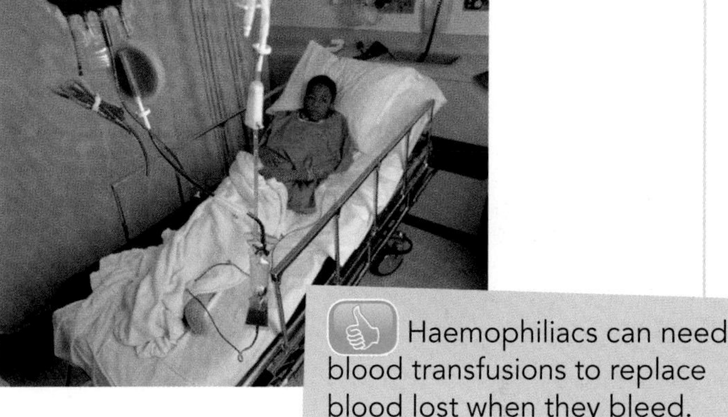

Haemophiliacs can need blood transfusions to replace blood lost when they bleed.

Drinks

Most drinks are solutions. Cola is a water solution. Some of the solutes in cola are sugar, caffeine, caramel, carbon dioxide and phosphoric acid. The solute carbon dioxide is a gas which makes the drink fizzy. Every time you open a bottle of cola some of the carbon dioxide gas comes out of the solution, making it less fizzy and eventually making it go 'flat'. Orange juice is another solution. Some of the solutes in this drink include citric acid, vitamin C (ascorbic acid) and the sugar fructose. The solvent in alcoholic drinks is also water, and one of the solutes is an alcohol called ethanol.

Urine

The urine that we produce is another essential solution. Urea is one of the solutes dissolved in urine that we need to get rid of from the body. Urea is a made when proteins are broken down inside the body. High levels of urea in urine are a

sign of kidney disease. Urea was the first **organic chemical** to be made in a lab. It was made by the German scientist Friedrich Wöhler in 1828 in an experiment which disproved the theory of 'vitalism'.

Friedrich Wöhler, the man who synthesised urea in the lab!

This theory stated that living plants or animals were needed to produce the chemicals found in living things. Today lots of naturally occurring chemicals can be made in the lab!

Emulsions

Salad dressing, milk and emulsion paint are not solutions. They contain tiny droplets of one liquid spread through another liquid. The particles in the liquids do not fully mix as we have seen in a solution. Some **emulsions** separate very easily. For example, a simple salad dressing can be made by shaking together oil and vinegar. If you do this at home you will see the small droplets of vinegar in the oil. If you stop shaking it the vinegar and oil will separate in a matter of minutes. Adding mustard to the dressing stops the two liquids separating as easily. Milk is an emulsion that thankfully does not separate so easily. It contains a water solution with tiny droplets of fat spread through it. The water solution part of milk has the sugar lactose, soluble proteins, minerals and vitamins dissolved in it.

The oil and vinegar in salad dressing do not mix!

QUESTIONS

1 Diet cola does not contain sugar. Look at a can of diet cola to see which solutes act as sweeteners.

2 Predict the pH of cola. Explain your answer.

3 Present a poster about the disease haemophilia. Name the solutes that are missing in the blood of people who have this disease and include other interesting facts.

4 Find out about some chemicals which are found in the human body which can be **synthesised** by scientists in the lab or find out about the scientist Friedrich Wöhler. Present your findings in a short essay or a poster.

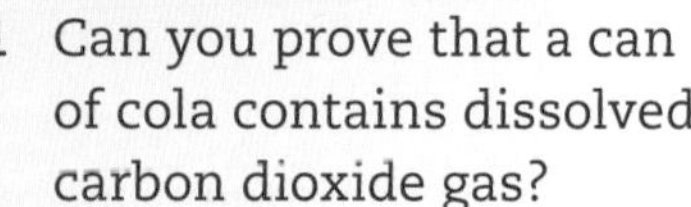

1 Can you prove that a can of cola contains dissolved carbon dioxide gas?

2 What would happen if you placed an unopened bottle of cola on a balance and then opened it? Would the mass change? Do the experiment and try to explain what happens.

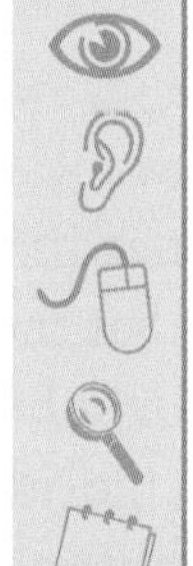

All come out in the wash?

The need for a variety of solvents

Detergents such as washing up liquid and washing powders must be added to water to help to remove the dirt and food stains on dishes and clothes. Detergent molecules are designed to be attracted to both the food and water to help them to 'mix' together. When the water drains away, it takes the food particles with it. Washing powders have to dissolve in water to do this job properly.

But have you ever got a grass stain on your trousers or a greasy chip stain on your top? It is not easy to remove these stains in a normal wash because grass and grease are insoluble in water. To get them out, special stain removing chemicals must be put on the stain before washing them or the clothes can be taken to the dry cleaners. Many stains on clothes can actually be removed by dissolving them in solvents which can be found in the house. For example, if you are painting a door with gloss paint, water will not clean your brush or any paint stains you get on your clothes. You have to use a solvent such as white spirit or turpentine to do this. Here are some other examples of stains which need special solvents to remove them:

Stain	Solvent
Tar, paint	White spirit or turpentine (turps)
Ball point pen	Glycerine
Under arm body odour	Baking soda and white vinegar
Tea	Lemon juice
Grass	Methylated spirits (meths)
Nail varnish	Propanone (sometimes called acetone)

Take care! When putting solvents on coloured clothes a lot of care is needed to make sure that the solvent does not dissolve the dye in the fabric. Solvent bottle labels always advise people to try the solvent on a part of the clothing that cannot be seen like the hem before removing a very noticeable stain. Some solvents may even dissolve the fabric!

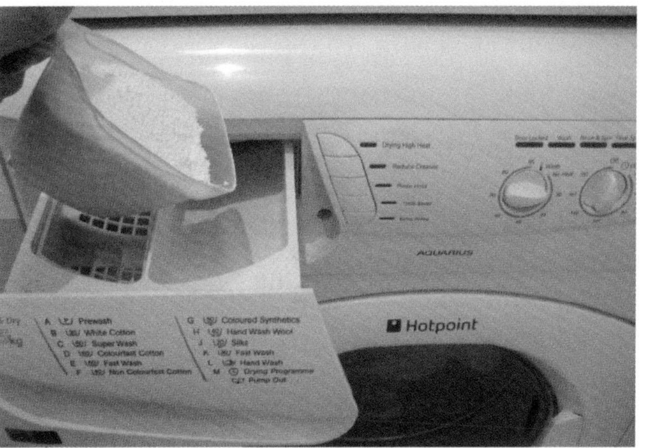

Hard to remove stains are removed in the dry cleaners using solvents like tetrachloroethylene (perc). Perc is known for leaving a 'dry cleaning smell' on clothes and is mostly used for fat-based stains. It is also in spot cleaners. It is **non-flammable** but can lead to colour loss. Items like plastic pens must be removed from pockets before dry cleaning clothes as the solvents might dissolve them, adding a dye to the clothes.

It's biological!

Biological washing powders cannot be used to clean wool or silk, because they cause tiny holes in these materials, which become visible after frequent washing. Biological washing powders contain **enzymes** which are the **catalysts** found in living things (see Chapter 1). The enzymes in biological powders break down **protein** food stains such as egg and blood. The problem is that silk and wool are also made of proteins, so the more these fabrics are washed, the more the enzymes will make holes in the fabric!

Hard and soft water?

Scotland and most areas of England have **soft water**. This means that there are low amounts of minerals dissolved in the tap water. This is good when you have a wash because you can get a lot of foamy lather with soap and shampoo. However, if you have a holiday in many areas of south-east England you will think that your shampoo is not working very well. The water there is hard and not only gives less lather but also leaves a white scum behind! **Hard water** spends a lot of time underground in chalky areas where it dissolves many minerals such as calcium carbonate, otherwise known as chalk. Calcium carbonate reacts with acids in soap to form substances which are insoluble in water and leave a solid scum around baths, shower heads and sinks.

Scum left behind when soap is used with hard water.

QUESTIONS

1. Why is petrol no longer used in dry cleaning? Think about the hazard symbol!
2. What kind of reaction happens when chalk (calcium carbonate) reacts with acids in soap?
3. Find out how chewing gum can be removed from clothes and furniture without using a solvent to dissolve it.
4. Who first developed 'dry cleaning' and where did their idea come from?
5. Investigate the effect of the solvent propanone on a polystyrene cup. Place the polystyrene cup in a large beaker before adding the propanone!

Active Learning

Activities

1. Experiment to compare biological and non-biological washing powders.

   Get two boiled eggs. Place one boiled egg into a beaker of a solution of biological washing powder and the other into a beaker of a solution of non-biological washing powder. Leave for a few days. Look at the effect of the enzymes in the biological washing powder on the egg white.

2. Experiment to compare soft and hard water.

   Use tap water for the soft water. Then make hard water by adding one teaspoon of plaster of Paris in 100 ml of tap water and leave it overnight. (Most of the plaster of Paris will not dissolve in the water and will sink to the bottom of the beaker). Then prepare 100 ml of soapy water by dissolving some soap flakes in tap water. Mix half of the soapy water with the soft water and half with the hard water. White flakes of scum should form in the hard water.

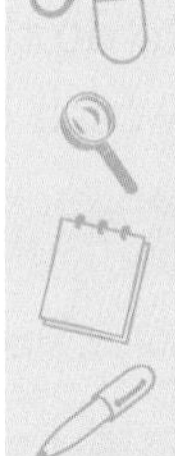

I'm saturated!

If you get caught out in the rain with no raincoat or umbrella, you get so wet that your clothes cannot possibly absorb any more water. A **saturated solution** cannot dissolve any more solute. The Dead Sea is a saturated salt solution. It has so much salt dissolved in it that you can float on the water and if you get it in your eyes it stings like crazy.

Active Learning

Activity

Make a saturated salt solution by dissolving as much salt as you can in a beaker of warm tap water. When the solution is saturated you will not be able to dissolve any more salt and will start to see salt at the bottom of the beaker.

Growing crystals

Crystals can be grown easily in the lab.

To grow crystals like these you need a small seed crystal and a saturated or **super-saturated solution** made using the same salt as the seed crystal. A super-saturated solution can be made by raising the temperature or pressure of a solvent so that it can dissolve more solute. Aluminium potassium sulphate (alum), Epsom salts and copper sulphate are good salts to use for making crystals.

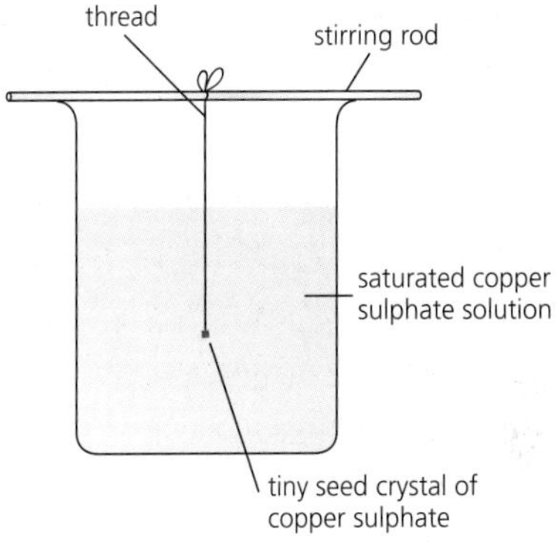

The salt solution that you place the crystal in has to be saturated, otherwise the seed crystal will just dissolve in it. It is usual to heat up some water, dissolve as much salt in the water as possible and then leave the solution to cool back to room temperature. This makes a super-saturated solution that should not dissolve the salt crystal.

Ask your teacher to demonstrate how fast sodium acetate crystals can grow from a super-saturated solution.

I'm saturated!

Some sports injuries are treated using heat packs like the one shown below. They contain a packet of super-saturated sodium acetate solution and a small piece of iron. When the piece of metal is flexed, crystals form very rapidly releasing a lot of heat.

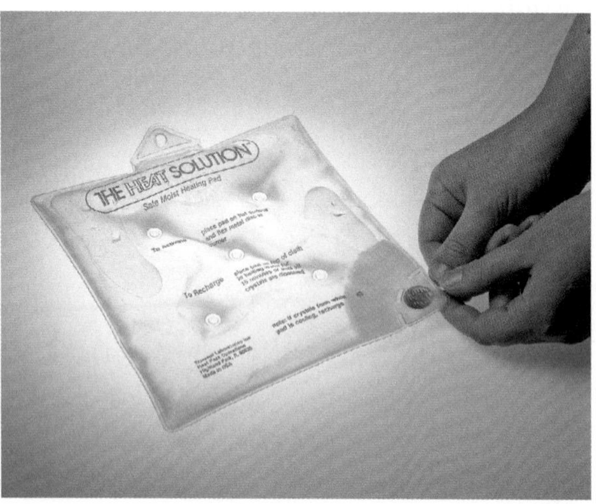

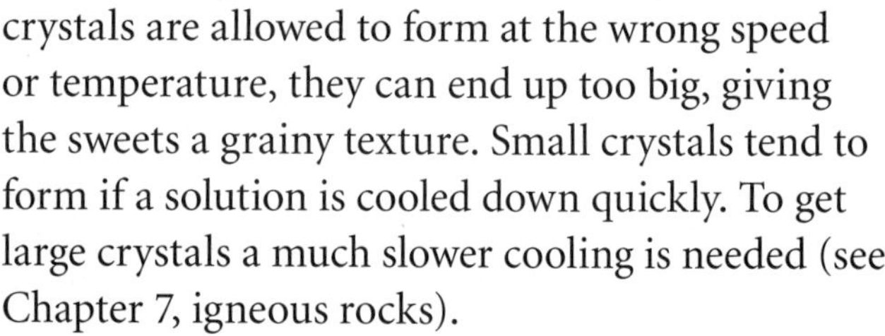

Making sweets like tablet and fudge involves making crystals from a super-saturated sugar solution. If the crystals are allowed to form at the wrong speed or temperature, they can end up too big, giving the sweets a grainy texture. Small crystals tend to form if a solution is cooled down quickly. To get large crystals a much slower cooling is needed (see Chapter 7, igneous rocks).

An example of a super-saturated solution is a fizzy drink. The pressure of the drink is increased to help more carbon dioxide gas to dissolve than would be able to at normal atmospheric pressure. When you take the lid of the drinks bottle this pressure is released and lots of carbon dioxide bubbles escape! Many artificial syrups are super-saturated sugar solutions.

Special study: Nitrogen gas and the bends

Deep sea divers breathe air from special gas tanks when they dive under water. As they dive deeper into the sea, the pressure increases and more nitrogen gas than usual dissolves in their body tissues. Their body tissues become super-saturated with nitrogen gas just as water becomes super-saturated with carbon dioxide at high pressure. If they do not follow the correct safety guidelines and come back up to the surface too quickly, the nitrogen gas comes out of the body tissues quickly giving the divers 'decompression sickness' or 'the bends'. This is where the nitrogen gas gets in between the joints of the body, causing the body to double up in pain. If nitrogen gas gets stuck in an organ of the body it can be fatal.

QUESTIONS

1 Find out where the Dead Sea is and what the salt in it can be used for.

2 Find out what affects the quantity of nitrogen that dissolves in the body tissues of a diver during a dive and how they make sure that they do not get decompression sickness.

Active Learning

Activities

1 Try making some tablet or fudge.

2 Make crystals from Epsom salts by mixing half a small beaker of Epsom salts with half a small beaker of hot tap water. Stir for a minute before leaving the crystals to form in the fridge. Fine needle-like crystals should form.

3 Draw a bar chart to show the mass of solute needed to make a saturated solution of these chemicals using 100 ml of water at room temperature (20°C).

Name of chemical	Mass of solute (g)
Sodium chloride (table salt)	36
Baking soda (sodium hydrogen carbonate)	10
Strontium nitrate	70
Sodium bromide	90.5

Solubility curves

A solubility curve shows how the **solubility** of a substance changes with temperature or pressure. The solubility of most solutes increases as the temperature increases. However, the solubility of gases like oxygen in water decreases as the temperature increases.

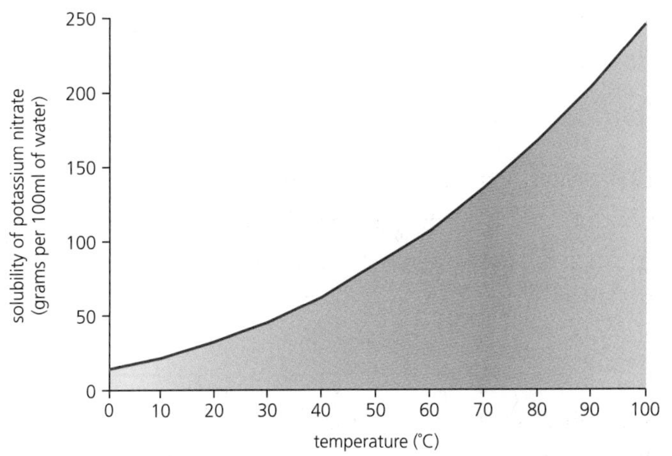

A solubility curve can also be used to predict the mass of solute that will come out of a saturated solution as it cools. As seen in the graph opposite, at a temperature of 100°C, 245 g of potassium nitrate can dissolve in 100 ml of water. At a temperature of 70 °C, 135 g of potassium nitrate dissolves in 100 ml of water. So if a saturated solution of potassium nitrate is cooled from 100 °C to 70 °C, the mass of potassium nitrate crystals formed will be the difference, 110 g of crystals.

Solubility curves

QUESTIONS

1 a) Describe how the solubility of sodium chloride changes with temperature.

b) What is the solubility of sodium chloride at 70°C?

c) At which temperature is the solubility of sodium chloride and potassium chlorate the same?

d) What mass of potassium chlorate can dissolve in 100 ml of water at 50°C?

e) What mass of potassium chlorate can dissolve in 50 ml of water at 50°C?

f) What mass of sodium chloride can dissolve in 20 ml of water at 60°C?

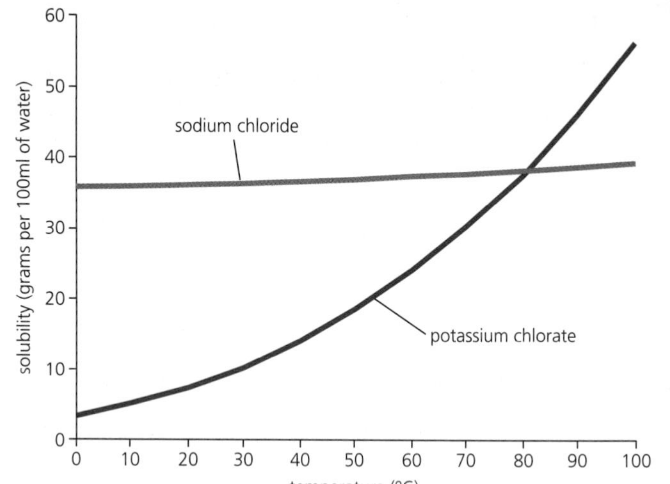

g) 100 ml of a saturated solution of sodium chloride is cooled from 80°C to 20°C.

i) What is the solubility of sodium chloride at 80°C?

ii) What is the solubility of sodium chloride at 20°C?

iii) What mass of sodium chloride crystals are formed when this solution cools from 80°C to 20°C?

2 a) Plot a graph to show how the solubility of copper sulphate crystals changes with temperature using the data below.

Temperature/°C	0	10	20	30	40	50	60	70	80	90	100
Solubility g/100ml water	14.3	17.4	20.7	24.2	28.7	33.8	44.0	47.0	56.0	67.5	

b) The next table contains the solubility levels for hydrogen chloride gas, but only at four different temperatures. Using these four figures, add a second solubility curve for hydrogen chloride gas to the copper sulphate graph, then use your new graph to estimate solubility levels for hydrogen chloride at 10, 30, 50, 70, 80 and 90°C (indicated by a *).

Temperature/°C	0	10	20	30	40	50	60	70	80	90	100
Solubility g/100ml water	82.3	*	72.1	*	63.3	*	56.1	*	*	*	

c) Compare the solubility of the solid and the gas as the temperature rises from 0°C to 100°C.

d) Can you guess which acid is formed when hydrogen chloride gas dissolves in water?

QUESTIONS

Extension question

3 a)  Oxygen gas is much less soluble in water than either copper sulphate or hydrogen chloride. Its solubility is measured in **milligrams** (mg) per 100 ml of water. One milligram is one thousandth of a gram. Plot a graph to show how the solubility of oxygen gas changes with temperature using the results below. (Note solubility is rounded to the nearest decimal point.)

Temperature/°C	0	10	20	30	40	50	60	70	80	90	100
Solubility in mg/ 100 ml water	6.9		4.3		3.1		2.3		1.4		0

b) Use your graph to explain why all oxygen is removed from water when it is boiled.

c) Why can a small increase in temperature lead to the death of tropical fish in a fish tank?

Active Learning

Activity

Plan an experiment to work out the solubility of copper chloride in g/100 ml of water.

GLOSSARY

Catalyst a substance which changes the speed of a reaction without getting used up

Concentrated solution a solution which contains a large mass of solute dissolved in it

Dilute solution a solution which contains a small mass of solute dissolved in it

Emulsion tiny droplets of one liquid spread through another liquid

Endothermic a process in which heat energy is taken in

Enzyme a biological catalyst found in living things

Exothermic a process in which heat energy is given out

Hard water water which has lots of minerals such as calcium carbonate dissolved in it

Hormone a chemical messenger produced in plants and animals

Insoluble a substance which does not dissolve in a solvent

Non-flammable a substance that does not catch fire

Organic chemical a chemical which is found in living animals or plants or in their remains

Physical change a change in which no new substance is made

Protein an important class of foods needed for growth and repair

GLOSSARY

Saturated solution a solution which can dissolve no more solute at a given temperature

Soft water water that contains low amounts of dissolved solutes

Solubility the mass of solute in grams that can dissolve in 100 ml of water at a given temperature

Soluble a substance which can dissolve in a solvent

Solute the substance (solid, liquid or gas) which dissolves in a solvent

Solution a liquid with a substance dissolved in it

Solvent the liquid in which a substance dissolves

Super-saturated solution a solution that contains more solute than is normally possible at a given temperature and pressure

Synthesise to make a chemical using a chemical reaction

MATERIALS

Earth's Materials

7

Third rock from the Sun

Level 2 What came before?

 **SCN 2-17a**

Having explored the substances that make up the Earth's surface, I can compare some of their characteristics and uses.

Level 3 What is this chapter about?

 **SCN 3-17a**

Through evaluation of a range of data, I can describe the formation, characteristics and uses of soils, minerals and basic types of rocks.

Third rock from the Sun

Our solar system contains eight planets which orbit the large star that we call the Sun. These are Mercury, Venus, Earth, Mars, Jupiter, Saturn, Uranus and Neptune.

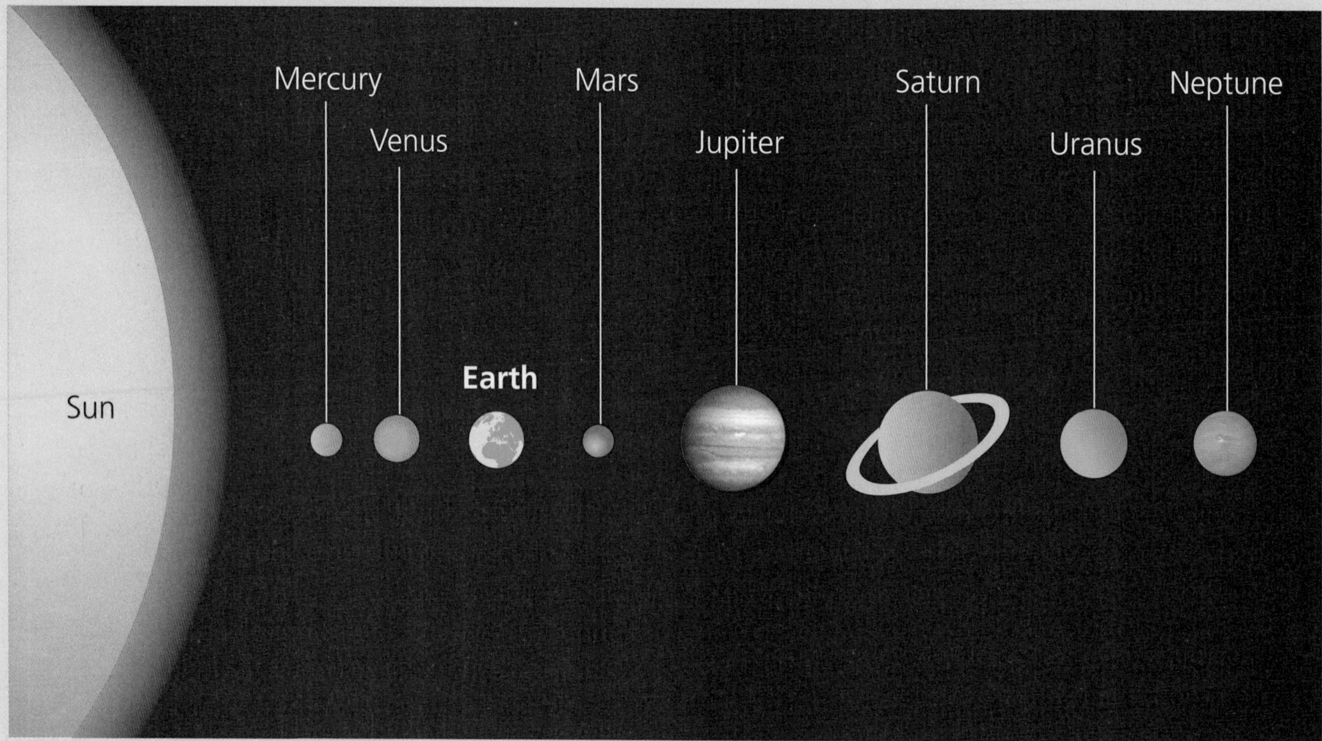

Mercury is closest to the Sun, then Venus and so on, until you reach Neptune which is furthest away. You probably do not think of yourself as living on a planet, and that planets are where astronauts travel to in space ships, but clearly you do live on a planet – planet Earth, or third rock from the Sun! Looking at the diagram, planet Earth is much smaller than some of the other seven planets, but to us it still seems quite a big place. It is possible for us to do a calculation which can give some idea of the size of the Earth.

Maths challenge – A journey to the centre of the Earth

The Earth is basically a sphere (ball) in shape, but for this problem you should think of it as a circle. The centre of the circle would be at the centre of the Earth. What is the distance from the circumference of this circle (the surface of the Earth, where we live) to its centre? You may have used a formula in maths when working with circles – it's $\mathbf{C} = 2\pi\mathbf{r}$ or $\mathbf{C} = \pi\mathbf{d}$ where **C** is the circumference of the circle (the distance all the

Maths challenge – A journey to the centre of the Earth

way round), **r** is the radius of the circle (the distance from the centre to the circumference), **d** is the diameter of the circle (twice its radius) and π is approximately equal to 3.14. If you rearrange the first formula you can get **r = C / 2π**. You would use this version if you knew the circumference of a circle and wanted to calculate its radius. So your challenge is this – the circumference of planet Earth is approximately 40 000 kilometres; what is the distance from the outside surface to the centre?

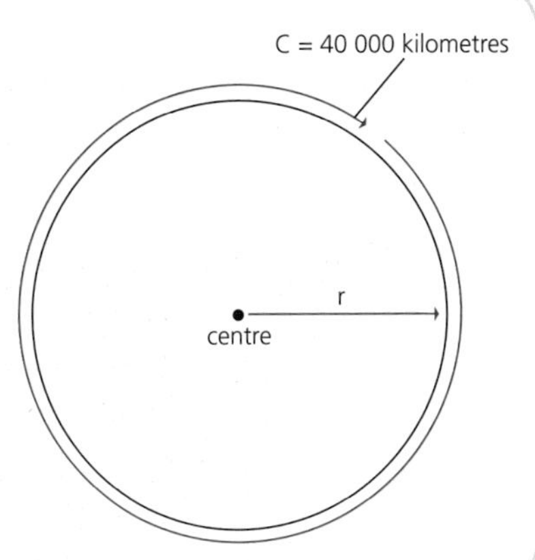

What are planets made of?

Vast amounts of money have been spent sending rockets and astronauts into space to collect samples of rocks and dust from other planets to find out what they are made of. It is hoped that one day liquid water will be found on another planet, meaning that there is the possibility of finding living things there similar to the living things on our planet! So far this has not happened, although in September 2009 tiny quantities of water were found in a sample of moon rock. But what is **our** planet made of?

Structure of the Earth

Imagine you started digging a hole on the surface of the planet. I suppose that if you kept on digging you would come out on the other side of the planet, but how deep a hole would you have to dig to get there, and would you have been digging through the same types of material all the way through? Let's look at a picture of the Earth's insides!

Atmosphere
Crust
Mantle
Outer Core
Inner Core

1 Outer core of molten metal
2 Inner core of solid metal

We live on the outside surface of what is known as the Earth's **crust**. The crust varies in thickness from place to place and is around 70 kilometres at its thickest. The thinnest part of the crust is beneath the oceans and is between 6 and 10 kilometres thick. To dig all the way through the crust then, the hole could be up to 70 kilometres deep. To us, that seems a long way down but **relative** to the size of the whole planet, the crust is thin! Do you remember your answer to the maths challenge earlier? After digging for 70 kilometres, around 1%

of the way to the centre of the Earth, you will reach the **mantle** – a thick belt around 2900 kilometres deep and made of both solid and liquid material called **magma**. Once through the mantle, you'll be in the outer **core** which is roughly 2300 kilometres deep and contains mostly molten iron and nickel, and well on your way to the inner core, where your journey will end – after 1200 kilometres you will reach the centre of the Earth. The inner core is solid, and almost entirely iron. The iron is believed to be responsible for the Earth's magnetic field.

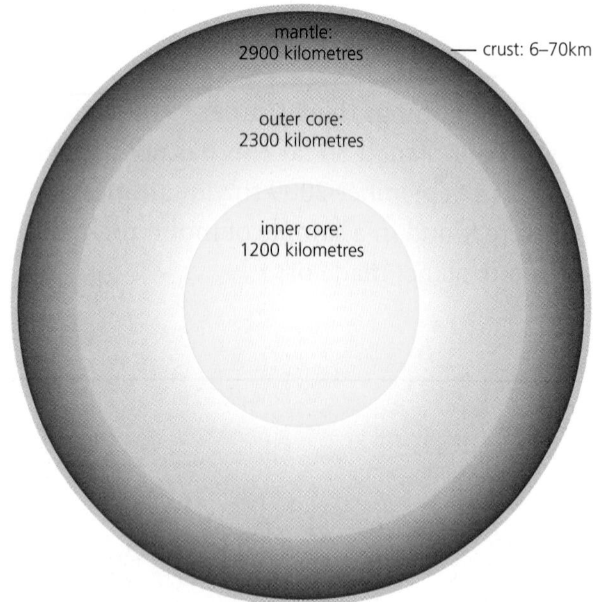

So unless you're a geologist (a special type of scientist), the mantle and the outer and inner core may be of little interest. We live on the crust, and it is from the crust that we get most of the materials which we use every day. But back to digging holes – what exactly are you digging through? What materials is planet Earth made of?

An American abroad

An American touring Scotland once pointed at the rolling hills and asked in all innocence: 'What are they made of?' How would you have answered that question? You may have used words such as rocks, stones and soil. But what are **they** made of, and are the hills in Scotland made of the same materials as the hills in other countries? The answers to these questions lie in the science of **geology**. Geologists are interested not only in what rocks, stones and soil are made of, but how they were formed. We need to know:

- Are all rocks the same?
- If not, in what ways might they be different?
- How were they formed?
- What are they made of?
- Are they of any use to us?

Rocks

Some very simple tests will show you that rocks are not all the same – they may be different colours, some may be harder or softer (try to scratch different rocks with a nail), or heavier or lighter (try weighing lumps of rocks of a similar size) than others.

Rocks are classified into three groups according to the way in which they were formed. Igneous rocks

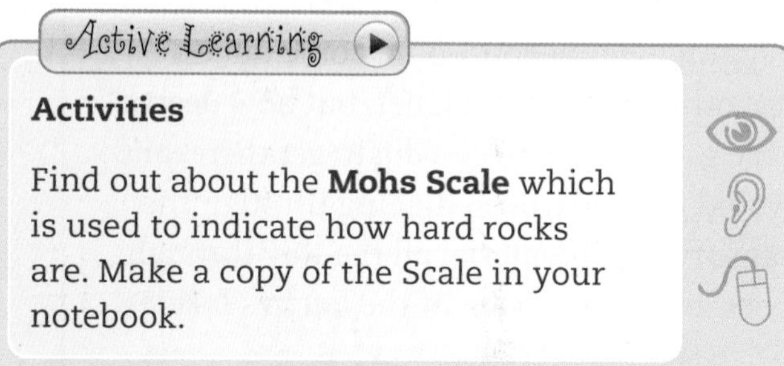

Activities

Find out about the **Mohs Scale** which is used to indicate how hard rocks are. Make a copy of the Scale in your notebook.

This photo shows six types of igneous rock. The left column shows (from the top): scoria, basalt, gabbro. The right column shows (from the top): obsidian, rhyolite, granite.

were formed when magma from deep beneath the surface of the earth cooled and hardened.

Magma is a liquid material found deep below the surface where it is very hot. Occasionally magma works its way to the surface, such as when a volcano erupts. There, it cools down and becomes solid.

Igneous rocks are fairly easy to recognise because as the **molten** material cools and hardens, crystals form. These crystals vary in size depending on how quickly the magma cooled. Slower cooling produces larger crystals.

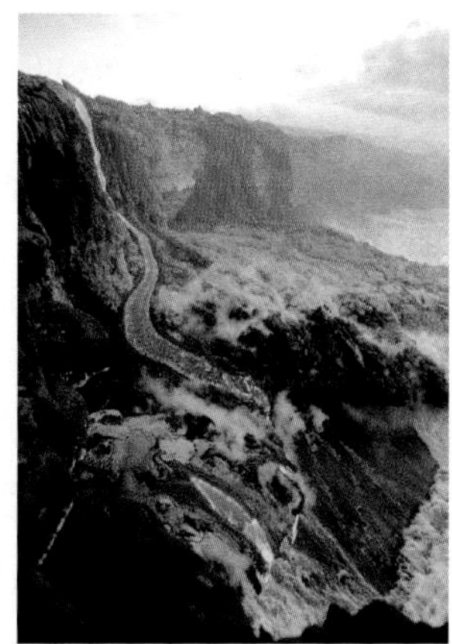

Active Learning

Activities

1 In March 2010 in Iceland, a volcano which had been **dormant** for around 200 years suddenly erupted. Research this event and write a report on its impact on the people of Iceland. Discuss also how people in other countries many miles away were affected by the vast clouds of volcanic ash produced.

2 There are volcanoes which are still active today. Find out about Mount Vesuvius. Write a report on what happened there in the year AD 79.

3 Find out about the origin of Arthur's Seat in Edinburgh.

Experiment

Ask your teacher if you can try this experiment for yourself, and be careful to take any safety precautions which you are given. Collect two watch glasses and place one in a warm oven and the other in a fridge. Heat a little salol gently in a test tube until it just melts. Place the two watch glasses on the bench and pour some of the molten salol onto each. Watch crystals of salol grow as it cools, and use a hand lens or magnifying glass to compare the sizes of the crystals.

Sedimentary rocks formed when fragments of existing rocks were broken off by weathering, carried in streams and rivers to the sea where they sank to the bottom and were squeezed together to form new rock.

Sedimentary rocks are where we find **fossils**. There are many places in Scotland where fossils have been found – from Sutherland to the Isle of Skye to the Victoria Park fossil grove in the west end of Glasgow!

Metamorphic rocks form when extra heat and pressure cause changes in previously existing rocks over a long period of time.

This photo shows five types of sedimentary rock. Clockwise from top left: limestone, quartz sandstone, gypsum, conglomerate, sandstone.

This photo shows five types of metamorphic rock. Clockwise from top left: anthracite, quartzite, mica schist, serpentinite, gneiss.

Scotland rocks!

Granite is an igneous rock found in large quantities in Aberdeen. Many buildings in the so-called 'Granite City' are made from this type of rock.

If you look closely at these buildings you can see the shiny crystals on the surface which were created when the granite was formed. Much of it was once mined from the Rubislaw Quarry, which has now been filled in. It was around 142 metres deep – about twice as deep as the Wallace Monument in Stirling is high! Basalt is another Scottish igneous rock. It can be found in several places in the UK including on the island of Staffa in the Inner Hebrides where Fingal's Cave is to be found. This is the place which inspired a famous composer, Felix Mendelssohn, to write a piece of music around 200 years ago. Try searching the Internet to see if you can find a way of listening to it – enter 'Fingal's Cave' into a search engine. Many buildings are made of limestone, which is a sedimentary rock. It is a very heavy rock and so not suitable for use in very tall buildings, although some tall buildings have a **façade** of limestone. Limestone is **calcium carbonate**, $CaCO_3$, and because it is a carbonate it will react with acid. This means that acid rain can damage limestone buildings over time (see Chapter 12). Limestone is found in Sutherland. The Old Man of Hoy is a famous landmark on the island of Orkney off the north coast of Scotland. It is made of sandstone, which is another sedimentary rock. Sandstone is very strong and more resistant to acid attack, so it is used as a paving and roofing material. It is also unaffected by very high temperatures, so it is also used to make fireplaces.

Uses of rocks

As we now know, some rocks are simply dug out of quarries before being cut or shaped and put to use. For example, granite (igneous), sandstone (sedimentary) and marble (metamorphic) are all used as building materials. However, much more interesting things can be done with other rocks – did you know that many metals such as copper, tin, lead and iron are actually produced from rocks?

Making metals

Imagine a world without metals – no aluminium cooking foil or drinks cans, no copper to carry electricity in cables, no iron to make steel which is used to make all sorts of things. Where do metals come from? One or two such as gold and silver can be found if you dig a hole in the ground in the right place – even in Scotland! In November 2009, it was announced that Scotland's first commercial gold mine was to be developed in the mountains around the village of Tyndrum in the West Highlands.

Tyndrum village.

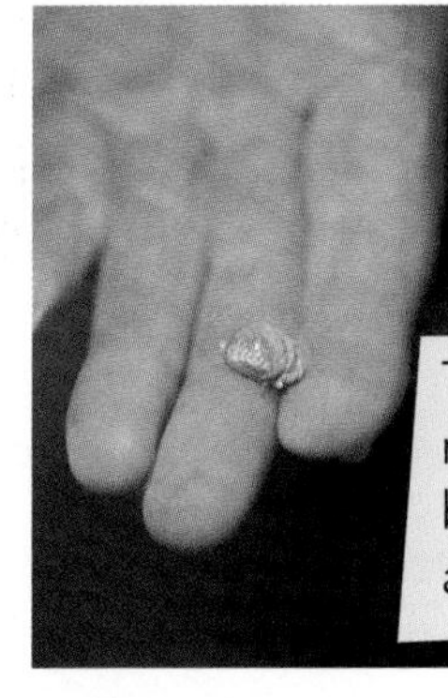
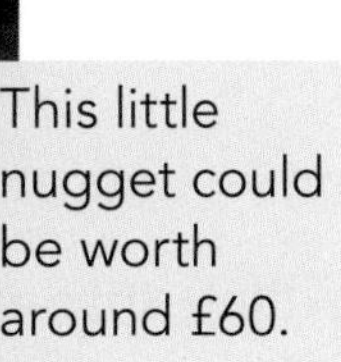
This little nugget could be worth around £60.

The mine is expected to produce around half a tonne of gold each year when full production starts in 2011. It would take about 100 kilograms of rock to produce just a single gram of gold, but at 2009 prices, half a tonne of gold was worth £13 million! It was expected that almost £1 million of silver could be produced too. It was not anticipated that large numbers of people from elsewhere in Scotland would head there to try to get rich quick! Yet when gold was discovered in America in the 1850s, a **gold rush** started. People travelled from all around to stake claims on pieces of land which might produce gold in large quantities, even although it was sometimes necessary to dig up tonnes of material in order to extract a few grams of gold. In other countries, this is exactly what they do to this day. So where do all of our other metals come from? Some of them are **extracted** from **compounds** contained in rocks known as **ores** (see Chapter 8). Others are made from compounds found in sea water. There are many mining companies which specialise in this kind of work, and one of the largest is **Rio Tinto**. It has operations all over the world – Europe, Africa, the Middle East, Australia, Asia, and both North and South America. Many of these mines work on the production of the same materials, such as aluminium and iron. However, some of them are unique, in that they yield large quantities of a substance not found in significant amounts elsewhere. Later in this chapter, we will look at some of the places where Rio Tinto operates, and some of the materials it produces. But how is it possible to turn rocks and stones into metal? Believe it or not, you can actually do it in a school science laboratory!

Malachite investigation

There are many ores which contain the metal copper, the principal one being **cuprite**, or copper oxide, formula Cu_2O. This compound is almost 90% copper. Another common ore is the green-coloured rock known as **malachite**.

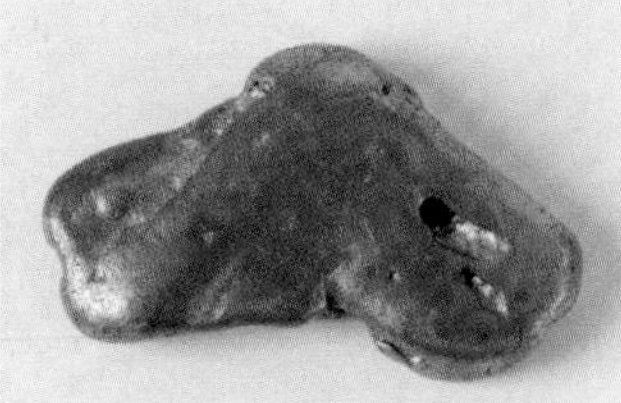

From this … to this!

It is a compound called copper carbonate hydroxide. Its formula can be written as $Cu_2CO_3(OH)_2$ or $CuCO_3.Cu(OH)_2$. It contains over 50% copper – much lower than cuprite, but still worth considering as a source of copper. Here are three possible ways in which this can be done on a small scale in school:

Note: for full experimental details search the RSC website.

- Roast some powdered malachite until it has completely changed colour from green to black. The black material is copper oxide, CuO:

  Malachite → Copper Oxide + Water + Carbon Dioxide.

  Once cooled, mix some carbon powder (which is also black) with the copper oxide, and roast the mixture. This should produce some brown copper:

  Copper oxide + Carbon → Copper + Carbon Dioxide.

- Add powdered malachite to some dilute sulphuric acid until the mixture no longer fizzes. This will produce a blue solution of copper sulphate:

  Malachite + Sulphuric Acid → Copper Sulphate + Water + Carbon Dioxide.

  Filter off any remaining malachite, and then carry out **electrolysis** (you will learn about this technique in the next chapter) of the copper sulphate solution. This will produce brown copper metal on the **negative** electrode:

- Make copper sulphate solution from malachite as before, and then **displace** copper from the blue solution using another metal such as iron:

  Copper Sulphate + Iron → Copper + Iron Sulphate.

Active Learning

Activities

1 The ores cuprite and malachite are good sources of copper. Find out which metals are extracted from the ores **bauxite**, **galena** and **cassiterite**.

2 The very reactive metal sodium is extracted from sea water. Find out which compound of sodium is present in sea water, and how sodium is extracted from it.

Rockin' all over the world?

In an earlier section of this chapter, the question 'are the hills in Scotland made of the same materials as the hills in other countries?' was asked. Let's do some travelling to some of the places where Rio Tinto and other companies work.

South Africa

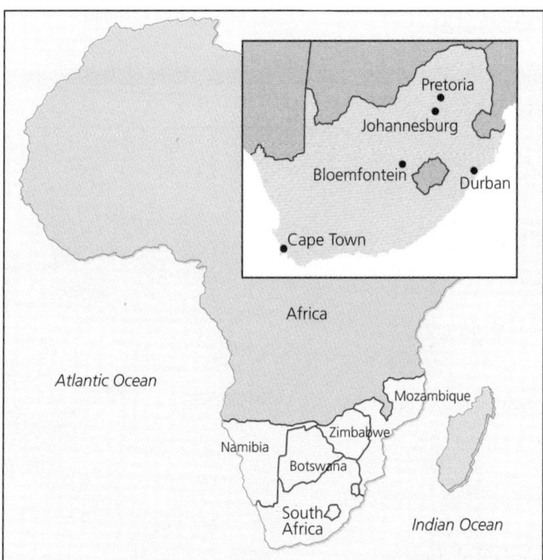

South Africa, host of the 2010 football world cup tournament, is a very interesting part of the Earth's crust. Many people will have heard of diamond mines there, but the Earth's crust in South Africa is also rich in platinum, manganese, chrome and vanadium – not to mention almost half of the planet's reserves of gold! How is gold produced? In the 1850s, and in some places even to this day, gold panning is the answer. This technique involves getting water to flow over material dug out of the ground in a large bowl or pan. The water washes all of the lighter, less dense material out of the pan and (hopefully) leaves behind tiny specks of gold.

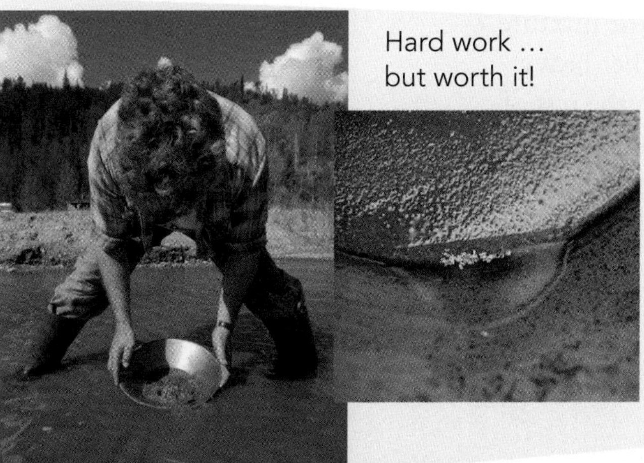

Hard work … but worth it!

Modern techniques used in South Africa are fully automated and involve the use of some clever machinery to replicate the panning process, but on an enormous scale. Some gold is also produced nowadays by electrolysis – basically special solvents are used to dissolve the gold out of the rocks and then the solution is electrolysed in the same way that you may have tried to produce copper.

QUESTIONS

1. Gold is expensive because it is rare, which means that there is not very much of it in the world. Why else might a metal be expensive?
2. Polished gold is very shiny and has a different colour to most metals. Find out and make a list of some properties of gold.
3. Apart from its use in making jewellery, what else is gold used for?

Brazil

Host of the 2014 football world cup and the 2016 Olympic Games will be Brazil. The football matches will be held at a variety of venues. The Olympic Games will be centred in Rio de Janeiro. Once the country's capital, Rio de Janeiro is a bustling city with a population of over 6 million people – almost twice as many people as live in Scotland – and it's only Brazil's second most populated city after Sao Paulo, which is itself the second most populated city in the world. From the rocks excavated in Brazil, aluminium, iron, chrome, manganese and tin are produced in large quantities. Gold and precious stones are also found in Brazil.

QUESTIONS

1 Which city is today the capital of Brazil?
2 What is unusual about this city?
3 When did it replace Rio de Janeiro as capital?
4 Which of the world's cities has the biggest population?

Canada

Kimberlite is a type of igneous rock which is of note because it contains diamonds.

Kimberlite

Kimberlite showing a large diamond.

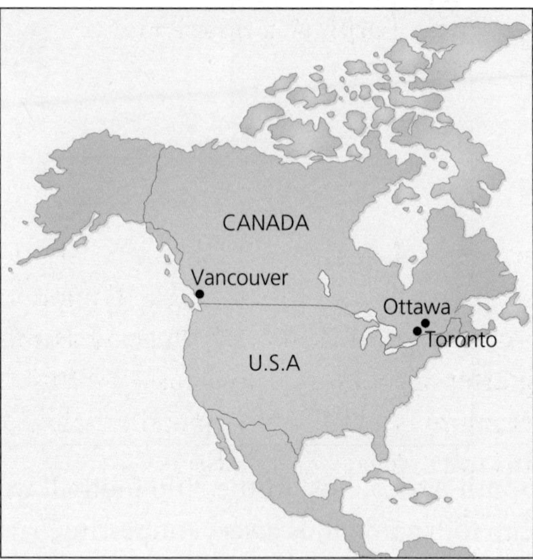

Kimberlite is found in a number of places in the world, notably the town of Kimberley in South Africa, which the rock is named after. Canada is also a source of kimberlite. It tends to occur in tubes or pipes which extend downwards into the Earth's crust. After mining, diamonds have to be extracted from kimberlite. In one of Rio Tinto's Canadian mines, up to 2 million tonnes of kimberlite are processed every year! The production of diamonds does not depend on any chemical reactions – it is the result of a number of physical processes. First, kimberlite is crushed, mixed with water and crushed again. A special type of sand is then added to the mixture which is eventually allowed to settle. Diamonds and other heavy minerals sink to the bottom and can be separated from the rest of the mixture and taken to another building in which the diamonds are recovered by an ingenious method. X-rays are directed at the mixture of solids causing only the diamonds to glow! This allows them to be separated from the mixture.

QUESTIONS

1 Diamond is a very pure form of one of the elements of the Periodic Table. Find out which element it is, and write a note on diamond's properties.

2 This same element is also found in nature in a quite different form. Try to find out what it is, and compare its properties to those of diamond.

3 Look up the meaning of the word **polymorph** and write it into your notebook.

Australia

Iron, nickel, aluminium, lead, zinc, silver, tungsten, manganese, gold and diamonds are all produced in Australia, which also has about a quarter of the world's low-cost uranium reserves. Uranium is a radioactive metal which is used as a fuel in nuclear power stations.

Torness nuclear power station, near Dunbar in East Lothian, on the east coast of Scotland. It has two reactors which can produce enough electricity for 1.5 million homes.

Much of the uranium in Australia has not been mined, mainly because of objections from environmentalists. Many people think that this is a mistake, and that nuclear fuel is the way ahead because it does not have to be burned in order to generate electricity. No burning means no dumping of gases into our atmosphere. Most power stations burn coal, oil or gas to boil water and turn it into steam. This steam is used to spin turbines which generate electricity, but the burning of fossil fuels produces gases which contribute to global warming (see Chapter 12). Nuclear fuels such as uranium and plutonium naturally give off radiation which can be used to boil water without being burned.

QUESTIONS

1 Uranium is an element. Look up the Periodic Table and write down its symbol, Atomic Number and Relative Atomic Mass. What does the Atomic Number tell you about a uranium atom?

2 Search the Internet to find the name of another element which is widely used as a nuclear fuel. Write down its symbol, Atomic Number and Relative Atomic Mass, and a note on how it is produced e.g. is it mined like uranium or is it produced in some other way?

Scottish nuclear

Did you know that roughly half of Scotland's electricity is generated in two nuclear power stations? Hunterston B is near Largs on the west coast, and Torness is near Dunbar on the east coast. At one time there was also Hunterston A power station, but it stopped producing electricity in 1989. The process of **decommissioning** then began, which can take 20 years or more to complete!

Scottish nuclear

In 2009 the Scottish Government was opposed to nuclear power generation, and had decided that the Hunterston B station should be decommissioned in 2016, with Torness to follow in 2023. No more nuclear power stations would to be constructed in Scotland. Yet in England and Wales, the construction of 11 new nuclear power stations was announced in November 2009. There are no problems of greenhouse gases and global warming associated with nuclear fuel. The major issue is the storage and disposal of nuclear waste, which is also radioactive.

Active Learning

Activity

What do you think? Should Scotland go nuclear or continue to invest in so-called greener alternatives? Prepare a talk to your classmates which presents both sides of the argument, and make a recommendation as though your group actually had the same responsibility and power as the government secretary for energy and climate change.

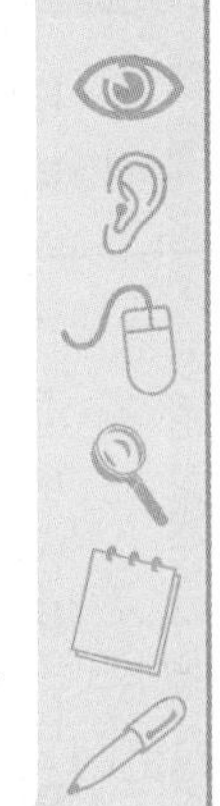

An inconvenient truth

Metals extracted from rocks found in the Earth's crust are widely used to produce many everyday items – from obvious ones such as gold and silver for jewellery and aluminium for cooking foil, to less obvious examples such as nickel for use in making batteries. The list of metals and their uses is enormous. So it would seem that the industries which produce these metals are of clear benefit to society. However, there is a downside. What effect does all this mining and processing have on countries where it is done and the people who live there? Yes, these industries do create employment, but what about their effect on the environment? And are there more sinister consequences of our demand for metals? These are the ethical questions which must be addressed.

Out of Africa

Are you one of planet Earth's almost 2 billion mobile phone owners? Or do you have a games console or a home computer? If so, consider this. There is an ore known as coltan from which the metal elements niobium and tantalum are produced. This ore exists in large quantities on the African continent in the Democratic Republic of Congo.

Much mining of this ore is done by hand – people with shovels digging holes in the ground to produce rock which can be crushed and exported to rich countries which have the technology to extract the precious metals from the ore. These miners are exploited by people who threaten them – they can be paid as little as one pound a day, yet the ore which they dig up can be sold on for tens of thousands of pounds to people who belong to multi-million pound industries which

An inconvenient truth

manufacture the power storage parts of mobile phones, games consoles, computers and even nuclear reactors.

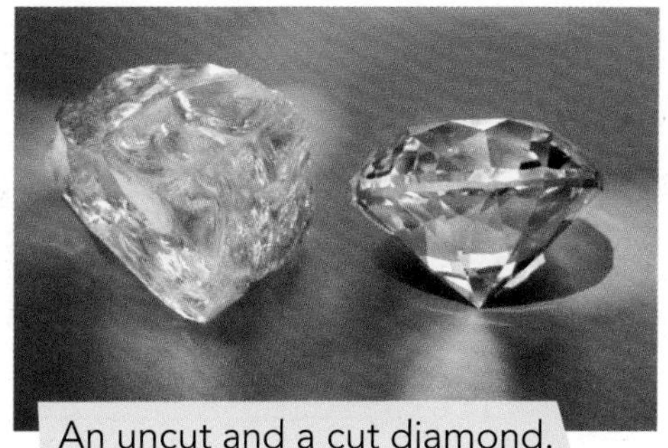
An uncut and a cut diamond.

Blood Diamond

This was the title of a film made in 2006. It was based on real events in countries such as Angola and Sierra Leone where rough diamonds have been traded for weapons by rebel forces. If you knew that a diamond you were about to buy had been produced in such away, you might not buy it. However, once diamonds have been cut and polished their origin is extremely difficult to trace.

Back to Earth – Soil

So what is soil? Is it a solid, a liquid or a gas? Actually it's a mixture of all three – tiny fragments of solids mixed with water and air. However, just like rocks, not all soils are the same. A simple way to check what your garden soil is made of is to shake some up with water and leave the mixture to settle. This is easily done in the laboratory using a boiling tube and a stopper, or even at home. You get the best results if the container you use is tall and thin. It can take a few hours or even a few days, but eventually you should see layers forming, because the biggest, heaviest solids in the soil get to the bottom first and the finest, lightest solids take longer to settle and so are found on the top. You may also see things floating on the surface of the water. This will be **organic** matter which has not yet **decomposed**, for example little pieces of leaves.

Soil is very important if you think about it. If you remember that all food chains and food webs begin with plants, and that on land these plants grow in soil, then it must be important. The roots of plants take in more than water from the soil. If you've checked your soil type and seen the different layers produced by solid particles of different sizes, you may not be aware that in amongst these layers will be more than just **inorganic** matter such as clay. Soil contains lots of other organic matter too – and not just worms! There will be insects, fragments of plant roots and seeds which might be visible if you look closely, but also **microscopic** living material such as **bacteria** which you won't be able to see. So soils contain lots of things in a complex mixture.

Farmers and keen gardeners constantly check their soils to make sure that the make-up of the mixture is correct. Changes in the mixture can affect how what is planted in it grows, so farmers and gardeners need to know some chemistry so that they can add things to their soil to keep the mixture right. For example, they might add fertiliser (see Chapter 10) if a soil was low in a particular **nutrient** or lime if a soil became too acidic (see Chapter 11).

Soil pH

You may think that a neutral soil with pH 7 would be the best environment in which plants would grow, and that if a soil was acidic plants would die. Some plants do, in fact, only grow well if the soil is neutral, but equally there are plants which will not grow well at pH 7. They prefer acidic or alkaline conditions.

Back to Earth – Soil

Plant name	Preferred soil pH
Carnation	6.0–7.5
Daffodil	6.0–6.5
Hydrangea (blue)	4.0–5.0
Hydrangea (pink)	6.0–7.0
Pansy	5.5–7.0

So soil is a vital part of the third rock from the Sun. To learn much more about it, read Chapter 1 of *Science for Excellence Level 3: Biological Science.*

GLOSSARY

Bacteria living things made up of a single cell

Core the central part of the Earth, made up of the outer and inner core

Crust the outer layer of the Earth

Decommissioning reducing radioactivity to a safe level which allows a site to be used for another purpose

Decompose to break down or rot due to the action of bacteria

Dormant a volcano that is not active but is not extinct

Façade the face of a building

Igneous type of rock formed from cooling magma

Inorganic the opposite of organic. Not related to animals or plants

Magma hot, thick liquid found deep within the Earth's crust which cools to form igneous rock after volcanoes have erupted

Mantle the part of the Earth between the crust and the core

Metamorphic type of rock formed when existing rock was changed considerably from its original structure and composition by pressure and heat

Microscopic very small. Cannot be seen with the naked eye, but can be seen under a microscope

Nutrient an element taken in by the roots of plants to help them grow

Organic related to or the remains of living animals and plants

Relative compared to

Sedimentary type of rock formed by the squeezing together of small pieces of inorganic and organic material which have been produced from older rock due to the effects of weather

MATERIALS

Earth's Materials

Useful substances from natural resources

Level 2 What came before?

 **SCN 2-17a**

Having explored the substances that make up Earth's surface, I can compare some of their characteristics and uses.

Level 3 What is this chapter about?

 **SCN 3-17b**

I can participate in practical activities to extract useful substances from natural resources.

Useful substances from natural resources

Planet Earth feeds us, clothes us and keeps us warm! In this chapter we will find out about how we get substances from the Earth such as fuels, metals and medicines.

Fossil fuels

Fuels are some of the most important substances on Earth. We use them to cook our food, heat our homes and to keep cars and trains running. Without fuels the world would be a very different place! A fuel is a substance that burns to release energy. It is the energy produced by burning these fuels that we use every day. When a fuel burns it reacts with oxygen; this is known as **combustion** (see Chapter 9). For example, when methane is burned in a Bunsen burner, the methane gas reacts with oxygen and energy is given out in the form of heat and light.

The oxygen required for combustion comes from the air. The bar graph on the right shows what gases and how much of each gas are present in the air that we breathe.

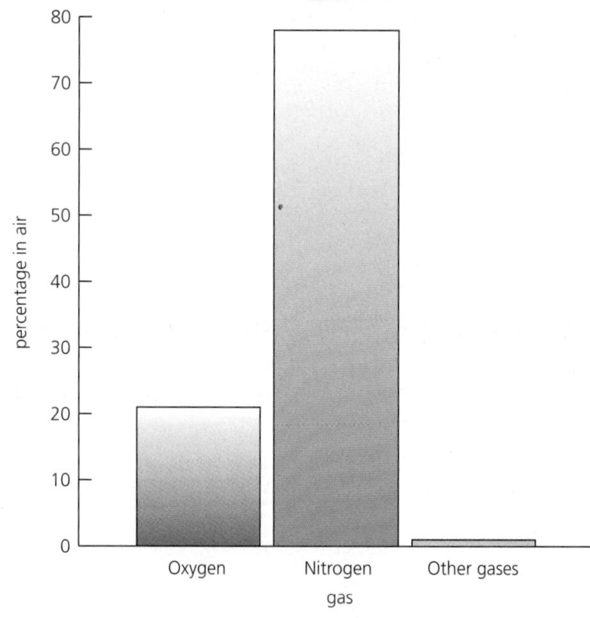

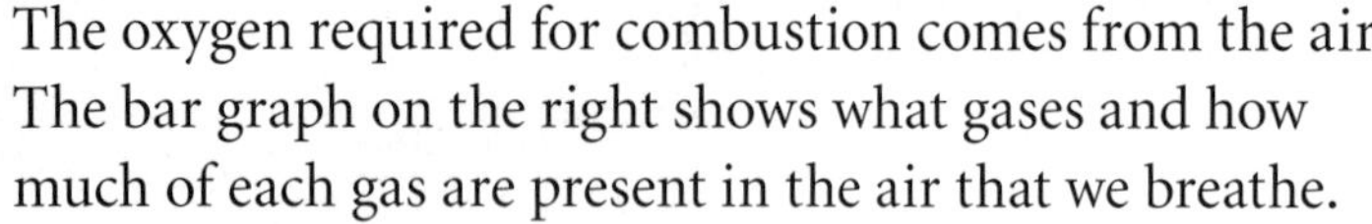

A simple experiment can be performed to identify oxygen gas. Oxygen relights a glowing splint.

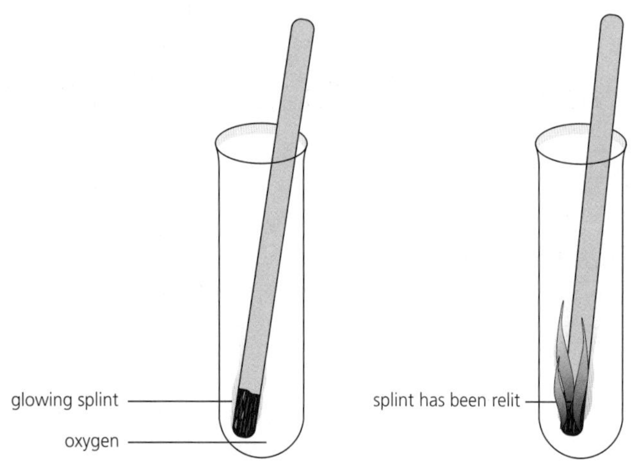

Your teacher may let you perform this experiment in class.

There are many substances which will react with oxygen to release energy. Wood can be used as a fuel, but some fuels release more energy than

Fossil fuels

others and are therefore more useful. There is a group of fuels that are very important because we use them to provide us with lots of energy every day. They are called the **fossil fuels**.

Coal, oil and gas are the fossil fuels. They are incredibly important substances in our modern world as they provide energy for transport, electricity and heating for our homes.

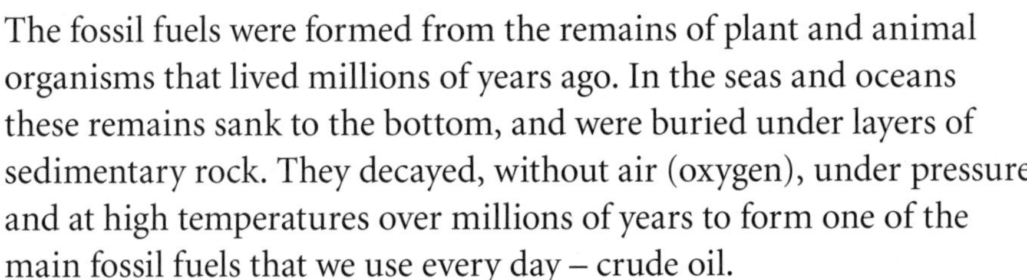

The fossil fuels were formed from the remains of plant and animal organisms that lived millions of years ago. In the seas and oceans these remains sank to the bottom, and were buried under layers of sedimentary rock. They decayed, without air (oxygen), under pressure and at high temperatures over millions of years to form one of the main fossil fuels that we use every day – crude oil.

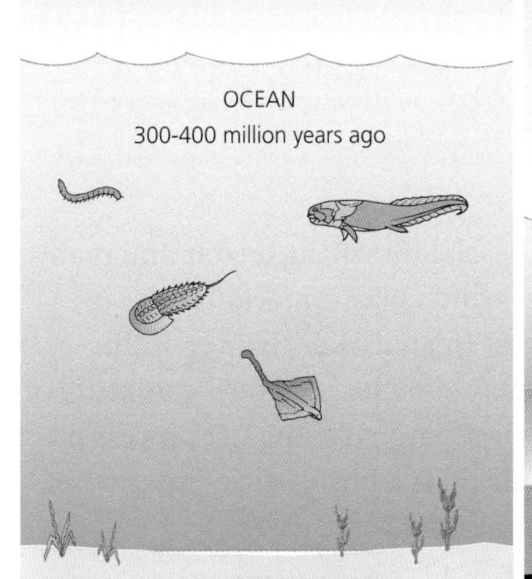

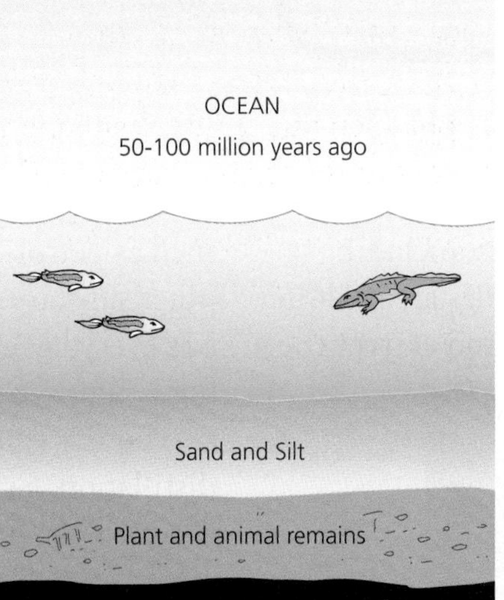

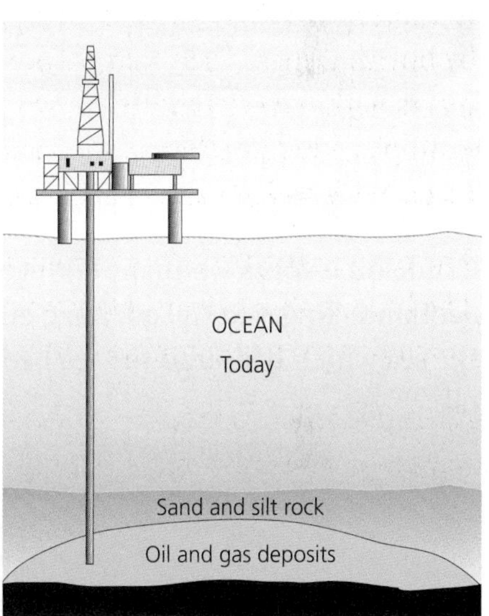

COAL
- → **Formed alongside dead plant material.**
- → **Used by power plants to produce electricity for homes.**

GAS
- → **Formed alongside both coal and oil.**
- → **Known as natural gas, it is used to heat homes.**

OIL
- → **Formed from dead sea creatures and plants**
- → **Has many, many uses, such as petrol, plastics, diesel, tar, lubricating oil.**

Fossil fuels

All three fossil fuels are said to be **finite**. This means that they are running out and cannot be replaced. Obviously when the fossil fuels do run out, this will have a major impact on our way of life. So scientists are currently developing alternative renewable sources of energy such as wind, solar and biomass.

QUESTIONS

1 Why are coal, oil and gas referred to as the fossil fuels?

2 Candle wax is a fuel.

a) Name the gas used up when a candle burns.

b) Wax is classed as a fuel. What is meant by the term fuel?

Active Learning

Activities

1 There is a fourth fossil fuel that is still used in Scotland. Find out what this fossil fuel is and how it was formed.

2 Scotland has Europe's largest on-shore wind farm. Whitelee Wind Farm produces enough electricity to meet the needs of Glasgow. Find out more about Whitelee Wind Farm and the plans to expand the site. Your report should include arguments for and against the wind farm.

Crude oil

Crude oil is found in many countries, including Scotland. To get to the oil, huge oil rigs are built in the sea which drill into the sea bed and extract the oil.

As crude oil is a **mixture** of many solids, liquids and gases, a special process must be used to separate it into its useful substances. These are all compounds which have essential everyday uses such as petrol, diesel, lubricating oil, tar and many other substances which play important roles in our everyday lives. In an earlier chapter of this book, 'Pure as snow', you learned how a mixture of two liquids can be separated using the process of distillation. Crude oil is a black, sticky mixture of many solids, liquids and some gases.

The useful substances found in crude oil are mainly:

HYDROCARBONS

HYDROGEN + **CARBON**

Hydrocarbons are compounds that contain hydrogen and carbon only. These hydrocarbons all have slightly different boiling points, which is very handy because this allows us to separate the mixture known as crude oil. However, unlike distillation, when heating a mixture of two liquids

allows us to separate one from the other, the separation of crude oil is much less precise. The process used is called **fractional distillation**, and it produces seven **fractions**, each of which contains a number of compounds which boil within a range of temperatures.

Fractional distillation

Fractional distillation is used to separate crude oil into fractions. A fraction is a group of hydrocarbons all with boiling points within a specific range. As each fraction has its own boiling range, when the gases produced from crude oil which has been previously heated enter the bottom of a high tower, each fraction will **condense** at a different height up the tower as the gases rise up the tower and cool down. The fraction with the lowest boiling point does not condense at all – it contains the hydrocarbons which are gases. The tower is known as a **fractionating column**, and the whole process takes place in industry in an **oil refinery**.

Grangemouth oil refinery on the Firth of Forth

Oil refineries are complicated places where lots of different industrial processes are carried out – fractional distillation is only one of them. The following diagram shows what happens in the fractional distillation area of the complex.

Crude oil

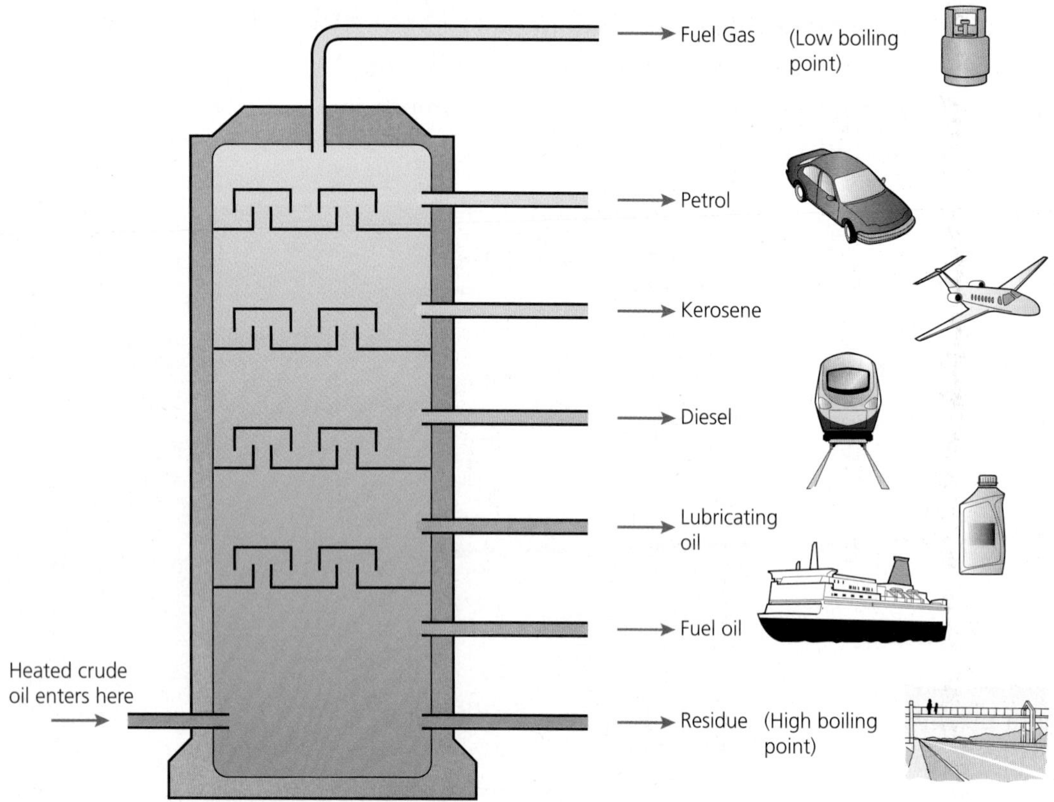

The stuff found at the bottom of the fractionating column is called the residue. It never actually boiled, because the crude oil was not heated to a high enough temperature.

The fractions produced all have many different uses. Their uses are highlighted in the table below.

Fraction	Uses
Fuel gas	Cooking and heating
Petrol	Fuel for cars
Kerosene	Jet fuel
Diesel	Fuel for cars, lorries and trains
Lubricating oil	Engine oil
Fuel oil	Fuel for large ships
Residue	Tar for roads

The fractions produced all have different boiling points, but they also show other differences in their properties such as **viscosity** (how thick the liquids are) and **flammability** (how easily they burn). The changes in boiling point, viscosity and flammability show a pattern.

The fuel gas fraction contains molecules which are very small, but the residue contains very large molecules. As molecular size increases both boiling point and viscosity increase, but flammability decreases. This is due to the change in molecular size. The larger a molecule is, the greater the forces of attraction there is between it and molecules of a similar size. This makes large molecules cling together more strongly than smaller ones, leading to a higher viscosity and an increase in the amount of energy needed to make them evaporate. Flammability also decreases as the molecules become larger.

fraction	boiling point	viscosity	flammability
Fuel Gas Petrol Kerosene Diesel Lubricating Oil Fuel Oil Residue	INCREASES	INCREASES	DECREASES

QUESTIONS

1 When crude oil arrives at the refinery it is separated into different fractions.

a) What name is give to the process that separates crude oil into fractions?

b) Which of the fractions is the most flammable?

c) Petrol and diesel can both be used to power cars, but which of these fuels is the more viscous, and which is the more flammable?

d) Give a use for the residue.

2 Copy and complete the following paragraph.

Crude oil is a mixture of ______________. It is separated by a process called ______________ distillation. Each ___________ produced has a different boiling _________. Most of the fractions produced are used as ________ but the most viscous fraction, ____________, is used as tar for roads.

3 The following fractions are found in a sample of crude oil obtained from Venezuela.

Fraction	Percentage in Oil Sample
Petrol	6
Kerosene	14
Diesel	20
Fuel oil and Residue	50
Others	

a) Which fractions of crude oil have been combined in the table as 'Others'?

QUESTIONS

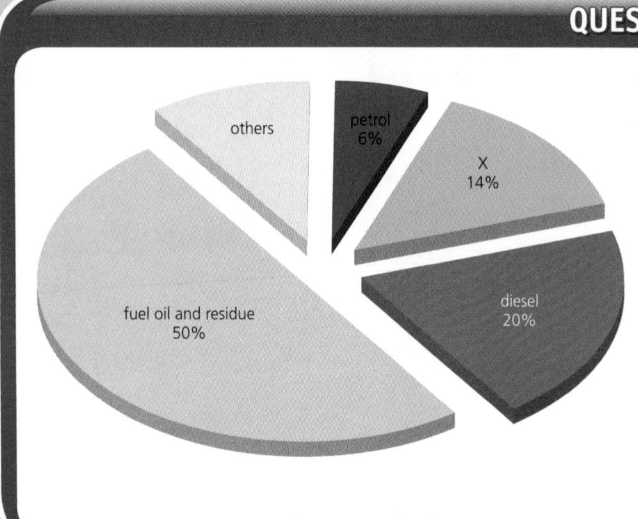

b) What percentage of the crude oil should be listed in the table beside 'Others'?

c) Which fraction is represented on the pie chart by the label X?

d) For which of the fractions shown in the table do you think there will be the highest demand? Explain your answer.

e) Present the information in the table as a bar graph and label the graph with the fraction names. Remember to give your graph a title.

Active Learning

Activities

1 Oil companies use a process called '**Catalytic Cracking**' to convert less profitable fractions into fractions that are in high demand and therefore more profitable for the oil companies. Find out about catalytic cracking and write a report which answers questions such as:

Why is it done? What is a **catalyst**? Which catalyst is used?

Draw a diagram of how it can be performed in the lab.

2 Grangemouth is a very important town for the Scottish chemical industry. Find out the answers to the following questions and use your answers to produce a short report on Grangemouth.

Where is Grangemouth – north, south, east or west Scotland? Which region is it in? Several large companies are located in Grangemouth. Name three of them. What do these companies manufacture? How many people do they employ, and what kind of jobs do they do?

3 Imagine your life without crude oil. How would your life be different? Write a short story about living in the world without crude oil OR write a newspaper story written the day after crude oil has run out.

4 Scotland has many off-shore oil rigs. Find out (a) where they are located, (b) who owns them, (c) how much crude oil is extracted and (d) how many people are employed. Produce a short report of your findings.

5 Nigeria is famous for its huge oil supplies. The Nigerian government and companies involved in Nigeria's oil industry have been accused of abusing human rights and damaging the environment in order to get maximum profit from its crude oil.

Find out about the Nigerian oil industry and the advantages and disadvantages it has brought to the country.

6 On 20 April 2010, an explosion on the Deepwater Horizon oil rig, 50 miles (80km) from Louisiana in the Gulf of Mexico caused the deaths of 11 workers and led to the eventual sinking of the rig. What followed this event has been described as an environmental catastrophe. Research

Active Learning

the incident and write a newspaper article that answers the following questions:

- Where exactly is the Gulf of Mexico?
- What may have caused the explosion?
- What steps were taken to clean up the oil from the waters of the Gulf and the coastline?
- How did engineers try to block the damaged pipeline to stop more and more oil from escaping?
- Why was the incident described as an 'environmental catastrophe'?

Pollution

Fossil fuels are very useful materials that provide us with lots of energy but they do have a major disadvantage. They contribute greatly to pollution. Two of the pollution problems that they contribute to are global warming and acid rain. These problems are caused by the gases produced when fossil fuels are burned. Let's look at four of the gases which cause these problems.

Carbon dioxide (CO_2)

Carbon dioxide is produced on combustion of any fossil fuel. It contributes to global warming (see Chapter 12).

Carbon monoxide (CO)

Carbon monoxide is a highly toxic gas produced by incomplete combustion. It is referred to as the silent killer because it has no colour or smell and is poisonous. Incomplete combustion occurs when there is not enough oxygen present to burn the fuel correctly which leads to a dirty flame and the production of carbon monoxide.

Sulphur dioxide (SO_2)

Sulphur is an impurity in fossil fuels. When burned, sulphur dioxide (SO_2) is produced. SO_2 dissolves in water to produce an acid. It contributes to the acid rain problem. **Acid rain** damages plants and speeds up the corrosion of iron structures and erosion of limestone buildings (see Chapter 11).

Nitrogen dioxide (NO_2)

Nitrogen is a very unreactive gas. Approximately 78% of the air that we breathe is nitrogen. However, when a large spark is passed through air, it can make nitrogen react with oxygen which is also present in air, forming first nitrogen monoxide, then nitrogen dioxide. The spark from a spark plug in a petrol engine also causes this to happen, possibly leading to car exhaust fumes containing nitrogen dioxide. This gas also contributes to acid rain. Interestingly, diesel engines do not have spark plugs, so cars with diesel engines do not produce this gas (see Chapter 11).

How can pollution be reduced?

Pollution can be reduced in a number of ways. Here are a few examples.

Lean-burn engine

A lean-burn engine increases the amount of air getting into a car engine. This reduces the amount of carbon monoxide produced by ensuring that the petrol has enough oxygen for complete combustion.

Catalytic converter

A **catalytic converter** is a special exhaust system containing platinum. It converts harmful gases into less harmful gases.

NO_X is a mixture of nitrogen monoxide and nitrogen dioxide.

Low sulphur petrol

Crude oil is mainly a mixture of hydrocarbons, but it also contains compounds of sulphur. These sulphur compounds can be contained in petrol as an impurity, meaning that sulphur dioxide is produced when the petrol is burned because the impurity burns too. Modern petrol has had **most** of the sulphur removed which means that less sulphur dioxide is produced.

QUESTIONS

1 Natural gas is mainly made up of methane. It is burned in gas fires, gas boilers and gas cookers. Every year in Britain around 50 people are killed by a poisonous gas produced by faulty fires.

a) Name the poisonous gas and give its formula.

b) Explain why this gas is produced.

c) What measures can be taken to prevent deaths caused by this gas?

2 All cars manufactured since 1992 have been fitted with catalytic converters.

a) Oxides of nitrogen and carbon monoxide react together in the catalytic converter to produce two less harmful gases. Name the gases produced.

b) Name a metal that is used in catalytic converters.

c) Suggest another way of reducing the pollution produced by cars.

3 Many car manufacturers are now producing **hybrid** cars such as the Toyota Prius.

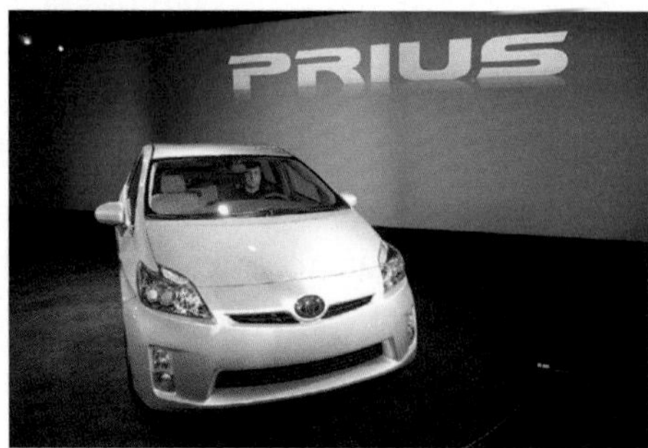

Find out what a hybrid car is and how it is reducing pollution.

It's a blast!

All of the objects shown below have something in common – they are made of metal.

There are lots of metals that could be used to make these objects, but all of them contain one metal in particular – **iron**. Iron is a very important metal because most of it is converted into **steel** which is used to make many things.

Unlike gold or silver, more reactive metals (see Chapter 9) such as iron are found in the Earth's crust as **ores**. The most common ore of iron is called haematite, which is mostly iron oxide – iron joined to oxygen. Haematite is found in many areas of the world.

To get iron from this ore we must remove oxygen and any other impurities. This is done in a **blast furnace**. The blast furnace is over 50 metres high and is lined with heat resistance bricks.

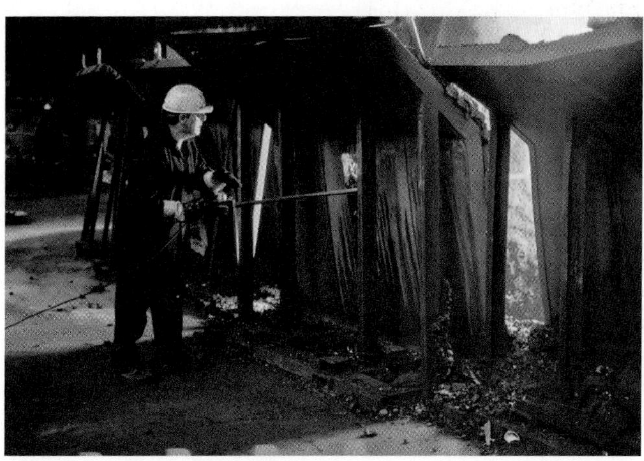

Shown here is the blast furnace at the Ravenscraig Steel Works site in Motherwell which was closed in 1992. A blast furnace involves a complex process that has two main stages:

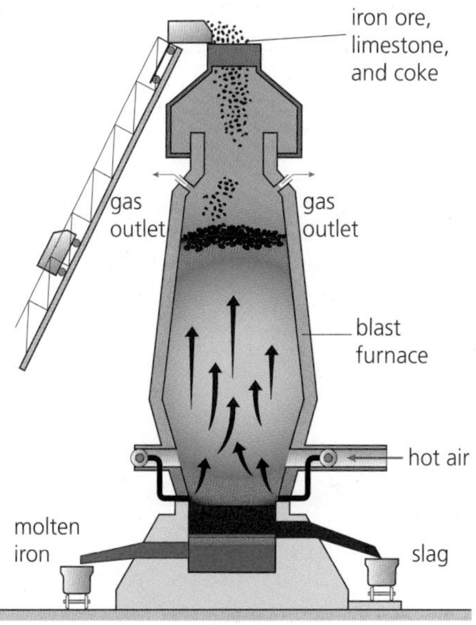

It's a blast!

Stage 1: Iron ore, coke (which is a type of coal) and limestone are fed into the top of the furnace. Limestone helps to remove impurities from the iron ore.

Stage 2: A blast (where the name 'blast furnace' comes from!) of hot air is fed into the bottom of the furnace to burn the coke which helps to take the oxygen away from the iron ore.

This process is performed at very high temperatures of over 1500 °C so the iron produced is molten (has melted).

Along with iron a substance called **slag** is produced. The limestone that was added to the blast furnace reacts with impurities from the ore and forms a slag. Slag is sold as a material for building roads and as insulation for homes.

One of the reactions that takes place in the blast furnace involves heating up limestone to produce a gas. You may be allowed to design and carry out an experiment that you could perform in the lab that will allow you to heat limestone and identify the gas produced. Include any safety precautions that will have to be aware of in your design. Check your design with your teacher before carrying out the experiment.

QUESTIONS

1 Shown below is a flow chart of the blast furnace process. Copy and complete the flow chart.

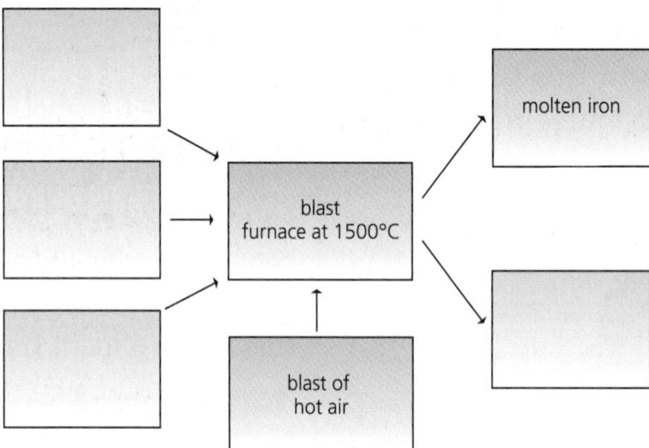

2 Shown in the table below is a selection of ores found in various parts of the world. After doing some research, copy and complete the table.

Ore	Metal produced from it	Where it is found
Bauxite		
Magnetite		
Galena		
Malachite		

Active Learning

The Ravenscraig Steel Works were closed in 1992 with the loss of many jobs. Do some research into the Ravenscraig closure in 1992 and give arguments for and against the closure.

Electrolysis

Another method which can be used to extract a metal from its ore is **electrolysis**. Electrolysis is the breaking up of a compound by passing electricity through it. Compounds which can be electrolysed contain metals bonded to non-metals, and they must first be melted or made into a solution in water before electrolysis can be carried out. When electricity is passed through a solution, the metal particles in the solution are attracted to the negative electrode because they are positively charged. The non-metal particles are attracted to the positive electrode because they are negatively charged. 'Opposites Attract' is actually a term used by scientists!

A diagram of how electrolysis is performed is shown here:

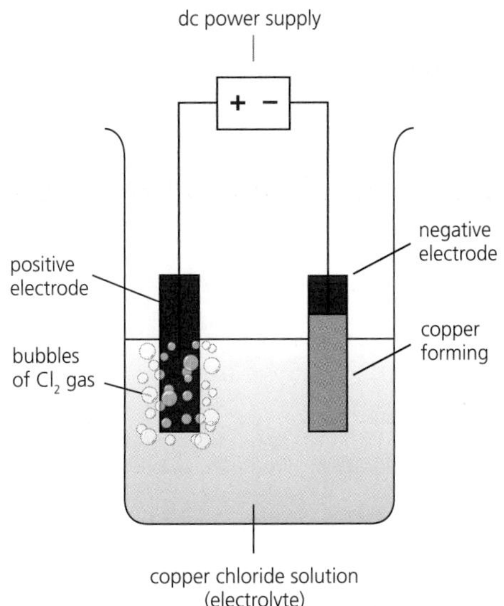

Your teacher may let you try this experiment in the lab.

Electrolysis of water

When water is electrolysed (see Chapter 2) it splits into two gases, hydrogen and oxygen. Hydrogen is being hailed as a fuel of the future and many car companies are already producing cars that run on hydrogen to replace cars that run on petrol or diesel.

In cars such as this, hydrogen reacts with oxygen forming only water, which means that no pollution is produced. The problem with hydrogen is that electrolysis of water uses up a lot of electricity. The electricity may come from power plants which burn fossil fuels, and so technically hydrogen may not be a pollution-free alternative. However, scientists have developed other methods of hydrogen gas production which may reduce the use of fossil fuels.

QUESTIONS

Lesley connected a DC power supply to two carbon electrodes that were placed in a solution of lead bromide. She recorded her observations in her jotter.

a) What type of experiment did Lesley carry out?

b) Name the gas that was produced at the positive electrode.

c) Name the silvery grey solid that was formed at the negative electrode

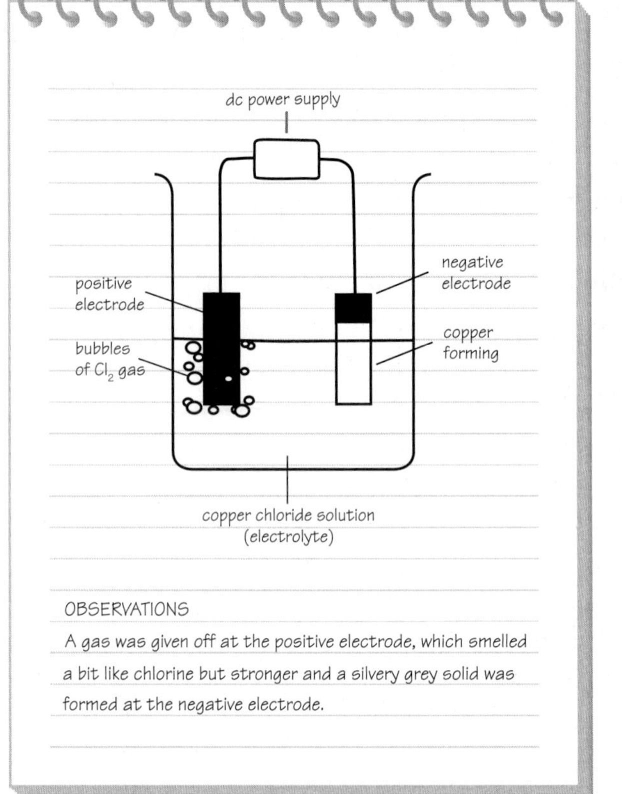

Active Learning

Activities

1 Cryolite is a very important ore.
Do some research on cryolite. Your report should answer such questions as:
   a) Where is cryolite found?
   b) What metal is extracted from it?
   c) How is the metal extracted from it?

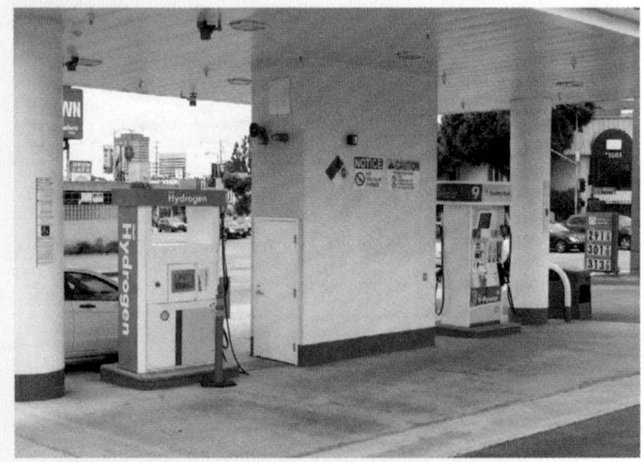

2 In America, the California Hydrogen Highway Network (CaH2Net) was started in April 2004.
The mission of the CaH2Net was to assist the move to a clean, hydrogen transportation economy in California in order to reduce dependence on foreign oil, reduce greenhouse gas emissions, improve air quality and grow the California economy. Research this project, and report on progress made since 2004.

Medicines

Your body must perform many chemical reactions to keep it working properly. **Drugs** are substances which have an effect on the body by altering these chemical reactions. Medicines are drugs that help the body when it is not working correctly; for example, antibiotics fight infections which can interfere with the chemical reactions in the body. Analgesics such as paracetamol and aspirin are used to ease pain.

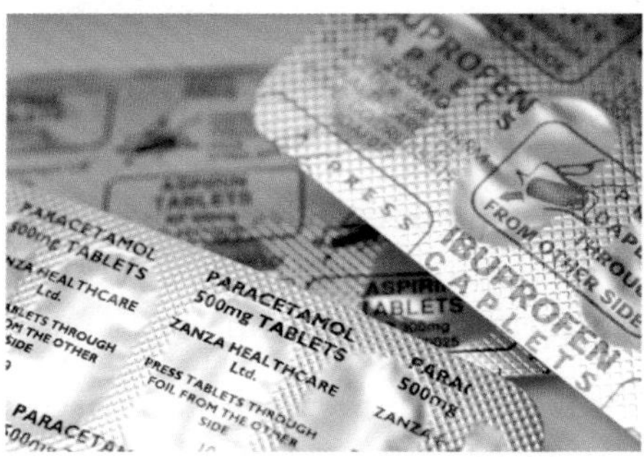

Medicines are mixtures of many chemicals but it is only the active ingredient that they contain which helps the body to work correctly. For example, shown here is the ingredients label from an aspirin packet.

Ingredients	Active or inactive
Aspirin	Active ingredient
Lactose	Inactive ingredient
Starch	Inactive ingredient

Only the aspirin in the tablet will help to ease pain. The other ingredients will not help pain but they are required for different reasons. Lactose improves the taste of the tablet and starch holds the tablet together. The active ingredient contained in medicines is often extracted from plants. Aspirin, for example, is based on a chemical that is found in willow trees.

Morphine, a very powerful pain killer, is extracted from a plant called Papaver somniferum which is a type of poppy.

Whereas medicines and alcohol are legal drugs, there are many that are illegal. Illegal drugs usually do not have a high degree of purity and because of this they can react very badly with the body which can result in the death of the user.

The drugs shown in this table are illegal.

Illegal drug	Effect
Ecstasy	**Hallucinogen** and **stimulant**
Cannabis	Hallucinogen and **depressant**
Cocaine	Stimulant
Amphetamines	Stimulant

These drugs do have medicinal effects and are used in medicines but when used incorrectly they have many unwanted side effects and can be addictive.

QUESTIONS

1 Match the class of drug to their medicinal effect.

Analgesics	Fight infection
Antibiotics	Ease acid indigestion
Antacids	Pain relief

2 Paracetamol is used in several medicines in different concentrations. For example, 1 teaspoon of Calpol contains 150mg of paracetamol. One Lemsip sachet contains 650mg of paracetamol and a paracetamol tablet contains 500mg of paracetamol.

Present this information in a table using the headings: Medicine, Quantity and Mass of Paracetamol.

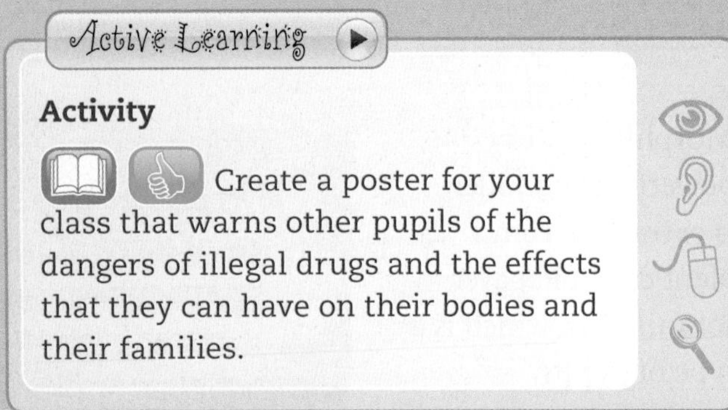

Activity

Create a poster for your class that warns other pupils of the dangers of illegal drugs and the effects that they can have on their bodies and their families.

GLOSSARY

Acid rain a form of pollution caused by gases such as SO_2 and NO_2 which dissolve in rain water lowering the pH of the rain water below 7

Blast furnace where iron is extracted from its ore

Catalyst alters the rate of a reaction but is not used up in the reaction

Catalytic converter part of the exhaust system of a car that converts harmful gases into less harmful gases using a catalyst

Catalytic cracking breaking up long chain hydrocarbons into smaller, more profitable molecules

Combustion a chemical reaction between a substance and oxygen releasing heat and light energy

Depressant a drug that slows the body's vital functions

Drug a substance that alters the normal function of the body

Electrolysis breaking up a compound using electricity

Finite a substance that is running out and cannot be replaced

Flammable a substance that burns easily

Fossil fuels coal, oil and gas. They were formed by dead plants and animals kept under pressure for millions of years

Fraction a group of compounds within a narrow range of boiling points produced from fractional distillation

Fractional distillation a technique used to separate crude oil into fractions with similar boiling points using heat

Fuel a substance that reacts exothermically with oxygen

Hallucinogen a drug such as LSD that causes hallucinations

Hydrocarbon a compound made up of carbon and hydrogen

Mixture two or more substances mixed but not chemically joined

Ore the state in which a metal is found in nature

Slag a by-product of the blast furnace

Stimulant a drug that produces a temporary increase in the activity of the body or body part

Viscosity the measure of how thick or runny a substance is

MATERIALS

Chemical Changes

9

Reactions of the Earth's materials

Level 2 What came before?

 **SCN 2-19a**

I have collaborated in activities which safely demonstrate simple chemical reactions using everyday chemicals. I can show an appreciation of a chemical reaction as being a change in which different materials are made.

Level 3 What is this chapter about?

 **SCN 3-19b**

I have helped to design and carry out practical activities to develop my understanding of chemical reactions involving the Earth's materials. I can explain how we apply knowledge of these reactions in practical ways.

Reactions of the Earth's materials

Our lives would be very different without Chemistry. Almost all of the processes and products that we take for granted can be explained through an understanding of the chemical changes involved. We obtain many useful materials from the Earth and our knowledge of how these materials react together has proved very useful. From heating our homes and powering our cars using burning or **combustion** reactions, to producing **alcohol** through reactions of **fermentation** and **distillation** (see Chapter 4) and preventing the unwanted reaction of rusting or corrosion of metals, reactions of the Earth's materials provide many benefits. This chapter will look at some of the chemical changes that are important to us.

Combustion

When a substance burns, it is reacting with the colourless gas oxygen from our atmosphere. We will begin this topic by looking at what burning actually is and the conditions needed for things to burn.

A combustion reaction is a chemical process that involves a substance reacting with oxygen gas. A fuel is a substance that reacts with oxygen to release energy. Only 20% of the air around us is oxygen. Both heat energy and light energy are given out by the process of combustion. As heat energy is given out by this process, it can be described as exothermic. What kind of energy is given out when a match burns? Energy is released as both heat and light. The energy we get from combustion reactions is very important to us in our daily lives; we use it to power vehicles, cook food and even heat and light our homes.

The conditions needed for burning can be summarised in the fire triangle. A triangle is a rigid, strong shape with three sides. A triangular structure like a playground slide would simply collapse if one side was missing.

The three sides of the fire triangle are oxygen, fuel and heat. All three of these are required for combustion to occur and fire to exist. If one side is missing, then the triangle collapses and the fire is extinguished.

Knowledge of the fire triangle is very important to us when it comes to fire safety. If a fire breaks out unexpectedly, we can control it in a variety of ways.

- When a bucket of water is thrown over a bonfire, it removes the heat and the fire is extinguished.

Combustion

- When a CO_2 fire extinguisher is sprayed on an electrical fire, the fire goes out because it is being starved of oxygen.
- When you turn off the gas taps in the lab, your Bunsen burner is no longer on fire because you have removed the fuel.

Fire safety is not as simple as grabbing the nearest fire extinguisher. You need the right tool for the job! If a puddle of oil was on fire, trying to tackle it with a bucket of water or a water extinguisher would result in the fire spreading. A foam fire extinguisher would safely put out the flames without them spreading.

QUESTIONS

1 Think about a burning match again.

a) What is the fuel used when a match burns?

b) Where does the oxygen required come from?

c) Where does the heat come from to start the reaction of the match burning?

2 Suggest how a fire fighter would extinguish fires in the following situations:

a) a chip pan has been left on accidentally and has caught fire

b) a forest fire has been burning for several hours and is moving closer to a village

c) two cars have crashed on the motorway and petrol has spilled underneath both vehicles and has ignited.

Active Learning

Make an informative poster showing the fire triangle.

Products of combustion

We know that in combustion reactions substances react with oxygen exothermically to release energy (both heat and light are given out by the reaction), but we do not yet know what are the **products** of combustion reactions. When an element is burned, it reacts with oxygen to form a compound called an oxide.

When carbon burns in a plentiful supply of oxygen, the colourless gas carbon dioxide is produced. Carbon dioxide is a **pollutant** gas. While it is not **toxic** it is still harmful to our environment as it contributes to global warming (see Chapter 12).

Products of combustion

In Chapter 8 you learned that most of the fuels we use today are **hydrocarbons** – compounds made from the elements hydrogen and carbon. Burning hydrocarbons produces oxides of these elements, namely water (hydrogen oxide) and carbon dioxide. So burning these fuels makes a futher contribution to the global warming issue.

When a hydrocarbon fuel is burned and there is not enough oxygen present, **incomplete combustion** can occur. Incomplete combustion is a dangerous problem as the carbon from the fuel does not completely burn and the poisonous gas carbon monoxide can be produced. Carbon monoxide is colourless, **odourless** and highly toxic so it poses a big danger to us. As we burn fuels in our homes for heating and cooking, there is a chance that carbon monoxide may be produced and so many homes have carbon monoxide detectors fitted to monitor emissions.

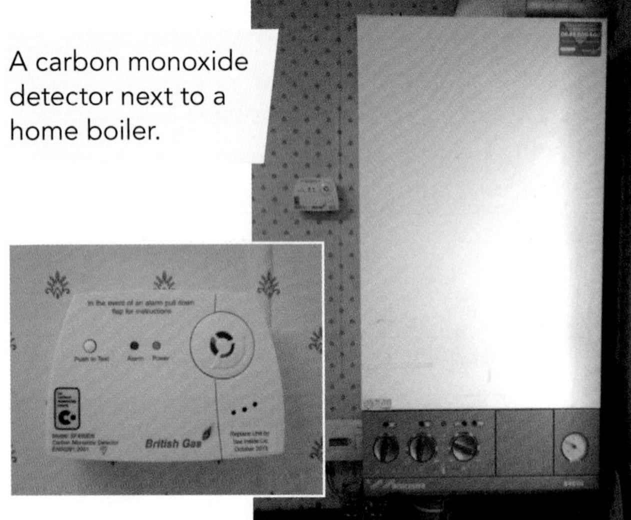

A carbon monoxide detector next to a home boiler.

Hydrogen is a fuel that is a safer alternative to hydrocarbon fuels. When it burns, hydrogen will form hydrogen oxide, better known to us as water. Water being produced from combustion reactions poses no pollution risk at all. Hydrogen fuel cells have been developed that could be used in cars instead of petrol.

QUESTIONS

1 Name two pollution problems caused by burning hydrocarbon fuels.

2 There are many different carbon monoxide detectors available. What important features do you think a carbon monoxide detector should have to keep you safe at home?

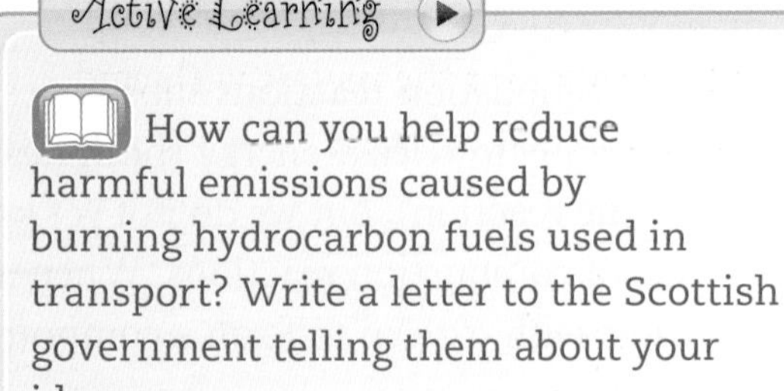

Active Learning

How can you help reduce harmful emissions caused by burning hydrocarbon fuels used in transport? Write a letter to the Scottish government telling them about your ideas.

Reactions of metals

In Chapter 8 you learned how metals are obtained from the Earth. Now we will look at some of the reactions of metals.

Water

Some metals do not react with water at all – just as well, or people would have to take off gold or silver rings every time they washed their hands! However, other metals do. Metals which react with water produce bubbles of hydrogen gas during the reaction. Your teacher may let you add pieces of different metals to water to see if you can spot which ones react and which do not. When you do this, you find that the ones which react do so at different speeds. Your teacher may then show you some metals which react quite spectacularly with water. At the end of these activities, can you draw up an **Order of Reactivity** – a list of the metals with the most reactive at the top and working down to the least reactive at the bottom?

Acid

Any metal which reacts with water will react even more vigorously with acid, once again producing bubbles of hydrogen gas. Some of the metals which do not seem to react with water clearly react with acid. And some do not react with acid or water. Once again, try to draw up an Order of Reactivity for the metals with acid. Compare it to the order in water.

Oxygen

Oxygen reacts with lots of substances. Your teacher may show you how to carry out experiments which allow you to observe the reactions of metals with oxygen. What is the Order of Reactivity this time?

The Reactivity Series

You should have found that the order was the same each time. The most reactive metals are always the most reactive – it doesn't matter what they are reacting with. The metals with medium reactivity are always in the middle of the series and the least reactive are always at the bottom. The order is:

1 Potassium — MOST REACTIVE
2 Sodium
3 Lithium
4 Calcium
5 Magnesium
6 Aluminium
7 Zinc
8 Iron
9 Tin
10 Lead
11 Copper
12 Silver
13 Gold — LEAST REACTIVE

(DECREASING ↓)

Corrosion: an oxidation process

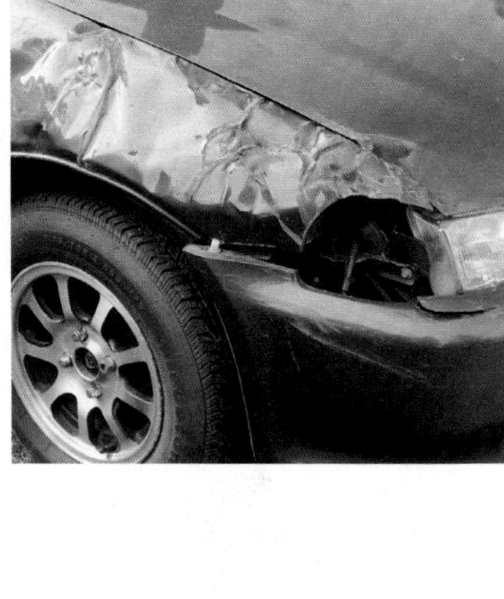

Have you ever left your bike outside in the rain? If you have not looked after it properly, you will not be able to ride it anymore because the chain will have rusted. Metal structures are always at risk of corroding. All metals can corrode and when iron corrodes we call it rusting. When objects made of iron become rusty, they lose their strength and can be easily broken.

When iron rusts it reacts with water and oxygen to form iron oxide. This takes quite a long time because iron is not very reactive, and the process takes place in a few stages. While iron is a very strong metal, iron oxide (rust) is much weaker. As oxygen is combining with the iron, rusting can described as an **oxidation** process.

We can show that iron needs both water and oxygen to rust with a series of tests.

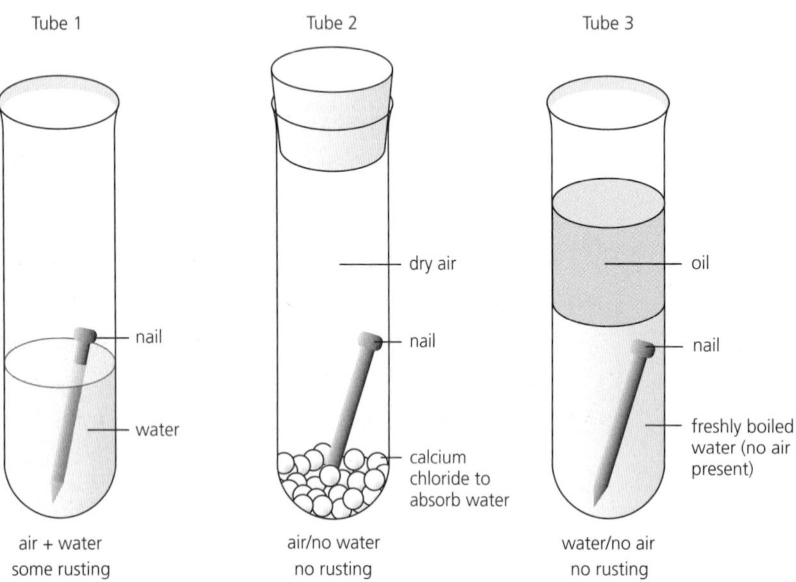

In tube 1, an iron nail has been left in water. As it is exposed to both water and oxygen, rusting will occur on the surface of the nail.

Tube 2 contains a nail in dry air. Some calcium chloride powder has been added to the bottom of the test tube to absorb any water from the air. With only oxygen present and no water, the nail cannot rust.

No rust is seen in tube 3 either. This time the nail is in boiled water with a layer of oil on top. The nail has not rusted as no oxygen can reach the surface of the nail to react.

Think about your bike again. Where do the water and oxygen come from that cause it to rust?

Metal structures that are exposed to the rain are in danger of corroding. Car bodies are always exposed and rusting is a real problem, especially here in Scotland.

Salt will speed up the rusting process. This is a problem for the hulls of large ships that sail in the ocean, as the salt water will speed up the rusting process. Another salt-related problem is that during the winter months, salt or grit is used on our roads to stop them from freezing. Unfortunately, this salt will speed up the rusting process.

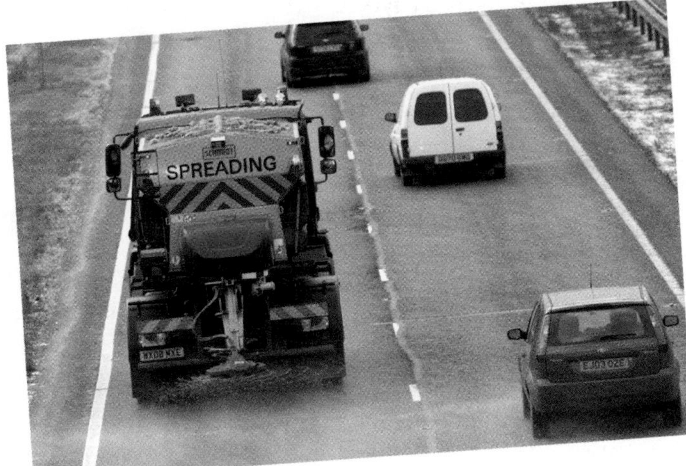

Acid rain will also speed up the rusting process.

By the time an iron or steel object has rusted, it is too late. The surface of the metal has been damaged and has to be removed, for example by rubbing with sand paper. In the lab we can test for the early signs of rusting using a chemical called ferroxyl indicator. Ferroxyl indicator is a pale yellow/green solution that changes colour to navy blue when an iron or steel object has started to rust.

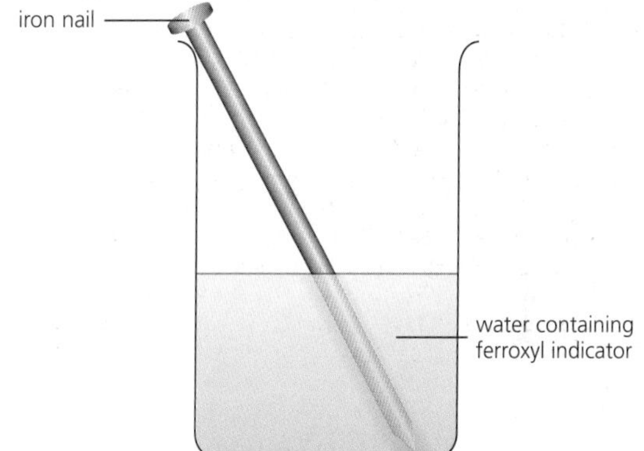

QUESTIONS

1 Answer these questions in sentences.

a) What is the name of the chemical compound that we call rust?

b) What substances need to be present for an iron object to rust?

c) Explain why an iron nail placed in a boiling tube of oil would not rust.

2 Some unreactive metals such as gold and platinum do not corrode at all, even when exposed to water and air. Can you think of two reasons why gold is not used to make cars and bridges?

3 Cars in warmer parts of the world are not as likely to rust as here in Scotland. Why do you think this is?

Preventing rusting

Rusting of metal structures can be a very expensive problem. Not many people could afford to replace their car every year if its body was left to rust. As rusting is a big problem for many of our metal objects, we must look at ways of preventing it. With small metal objects like bikes it can be very simple; however, some objects cannot be put away in your shed! Structures like bridges and cargo ships will always be exposed to both water and oxygen, so how can we prevent rusting?

Physical (or barrier) protection stops the water or oxygen from reaching the surface of the metal. As both water and oxygen are needed for corrosion, if one is missing then the reaction does not happen. This can be as easy as creating a barrier on the surface of the metal by coating it. Coatings like paint are suitable for structures such as car bodies and other larger objects. Paint would be a good choice for the frame of a bike, but what about the chain? It has to be free to bend and move. Bike chains and moving parts of machines are coated in oil or grease to prevent rusting.

Metal objects can also be coated in less reactive metals. This process is known as electroplating. The metal is given an outside coating that will not rust when exposed to water and oxygen and so the metal inside is protected. When chromium is used, it leaves the object looking shiny and attractive and safe from rust!

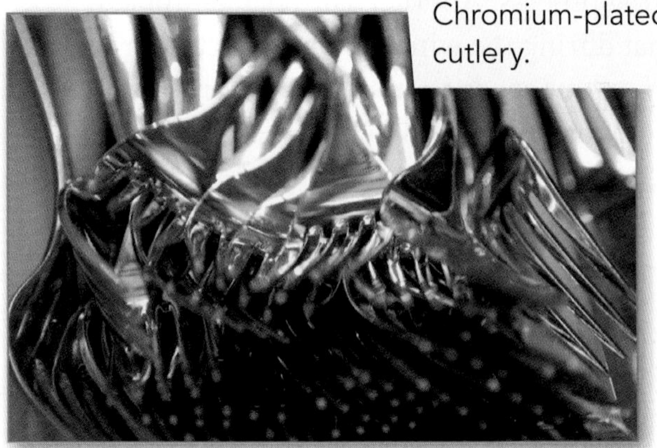

Chromium-plated cutlery.

One of the best ways of stopping iron objects from rusting is by the process of **galvanising**. Galvanising coats the iron in a layer of zinc. Not only does the zinc act as a barrier protecting the iron from rusting but it will also prevent rusting even if the zinc coating becomes damaged. As zinc is a more reactive metal than iron, it will sacrifice itself by corroding, leaving the iron as strong as ever.

Clydeside Galvanisers' yard in Glasgow.

Some metals will not offer good protection to iron and steel if they are used as coatings.

The two iron nails here have been wrapped in different metals and then left in water.

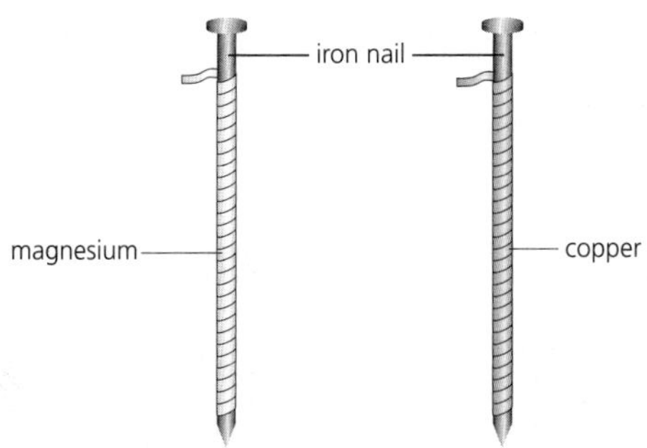

When ferroxyl indicator is added, it shows a blue colour around the nail wrapped in copper, indicating rust is present. No blue colour is present around the nail wrapped in magnesium; instead a pink colour is visible. This pink colour formed around the nail wrapped in magnesium suggests that no rusting has occurred.

QUESTIONS

1 Complete the table below giving an appropriate method of protecting the metal from corrosion.

Iron object	Method of protection used
Knife, fork and spoon set	
Bicycle chain	
Garden gate	
Hull of a ship	

2 Why does painting a steel fence protect it from corrosion?

3 What metal is used in the process of galvanising?

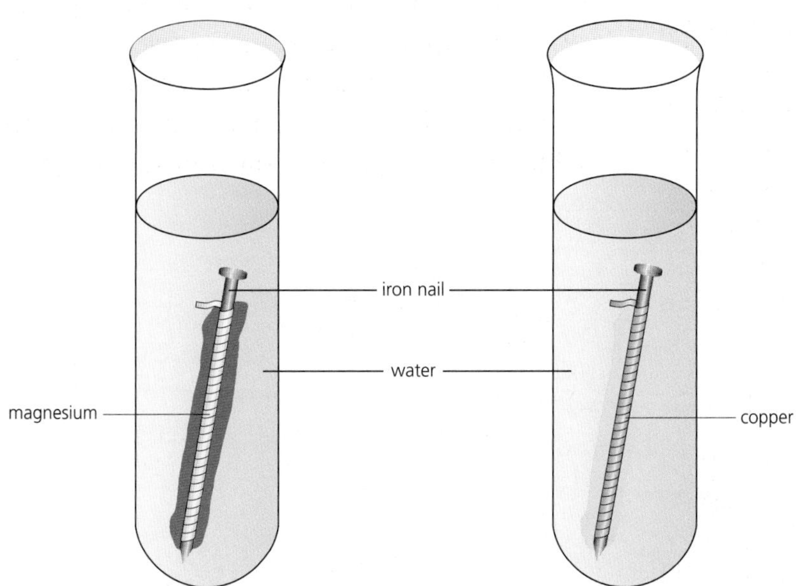

The magnesium has protected the iron nail. As magnesium is a more reactive metal, it reacts more quickly than iron and will corrode, keeping the iron intact. Copper is a poor choice for coating iron objects. Copper is less reactive than iron, which causes the iron to rust more quickly than it would have if no copper was present.

GLOSSARY

Alcohol a type of chemical compound

Combustion the chemical name for burning when substances react with oxygen and release energy

Corrosion a chemical reaction that occurs between metals and oxygen on the surface of the metal changing the metal from an element to a compound

Distillation a process used to purify a mixture of liquids (like alcohol and water) using the different boiling points of each liquid

Fermentation the chemical process used to make alcohol from plant sources

Galvanising a process that helps prevent rusting by coating iron with a protective layer of zinc

Hydrocarbon a compound that contains carbon and hydrogen ONLY

Incomplete combustion name given to the reaction when a fuel burns in a low supply of oxygen

Odourless something that has no smell

Oxidation a chemical reaction where oxygen is added onto other elements. Examples include combustion and corrosion

Pollutant a general term for a substance harmful to our environment

Product the new substance that is made in any chemical reaction

Toxic a substance that is poisonous and can cause death

PLANET EARTH

Biodiversity and Interdependence

Feeding the world

Level 2 What came before?

 **SCN 2-03a**

I have collaborated in the design of an investigation into the effects of fertilisers on the growth of plants. I can express an informed view of the risks and benefits of their use.

Level 3 What is this chapter about?

 **SCN 3-03a**

Through investigations based on experimental evidence I can explain the use of many types of chemicals in agriculture and their alternatives and can evaluate their potential impact on the world's food production.

Feeding the world

The POPClock

According to the world population clock (POPClock) there are around 7000 million people living on planet Earth.

That's a lot of mouths to feed!

In this chapter we will look at a variety of the natural and artificial chemicals that are used to increase food production on planet Earth today and since prehistoric times!

Active Learning

Activities

1 Find out exactly how many people are currently living on this planet using the world POPClock. This web link is http://www.census.gov/main/www/popclock.html.

2 Zimbabwe was once called the 'bread basket of Africa'. Find out why it was called this and why today a huge percentage of people in Zimbabwe do not have enough to eat.

3 Write an essay or draw a cartoon about a country that is currently finding it hard to produce enough crops to feed its population.

4 **Bioethanol** is a renewable liquid fuel which can be mixed with petrol and used as a fuel in cars. However, a lot of the land that is being used to grow the crops used to make bioethanol used to be used to produce food crops for the local people. Discuss the use of land in developing countries to grow crops for making bioethanol. One group could present the value of growing crops for bioethanol and another could promote the need of the local people for food.

Plants need chemicals to survive!

Do you know of anybody who is really good at killing plants? We have all seen plants that are wilting or have yellow leaves due to neglect. Plants make their own food from two chemicals – water and carbon dioxide. Plants can get all the carbon dioxide they need from the air but they wilt if they do not get enough water. But why do they sometimes look like this?

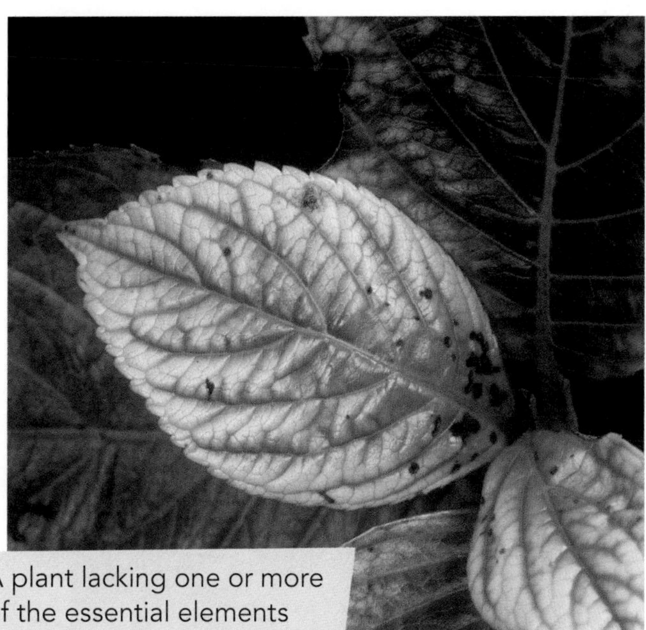

A plant lacking one or more of the essential elements needed for healthy growth.

Plants need about 16 different chemicals called **essential elements** for proper growth. Three of these essential elements are nitrogen, phosphorous and potassium. This table shows what these elements are needed for.

Essential element	Chemical symbol	Use
Nitrogen	N	Making plant proteins in leaves and stalks
Phosphorous	P	Making plant enzymes
Potassium	K	Controls the rate of photosynthesis and other chemical reactions in the plant

Plants usually get these elements (N, P and K) in the form of soluble compounds which are dissolved in the water taken up by their roots. **Leguminous** plants do not need to take up nitrogen through their roots because they have 'friendly bacteria' contained in little 'bumps' on their roots called root nodules which get nitrogen for them. The scientific name for these bacteria is '**nitrifying bacteria**'. Clover, beans, lentils, peas and peanuts are examples of leguminous plants. Nitrifying bacteria 'fix' nitrogen from the air; this means that they convert it into nitrogen compounds which can be used by the plant.

Root nodules on the roots of a leguminous plant.

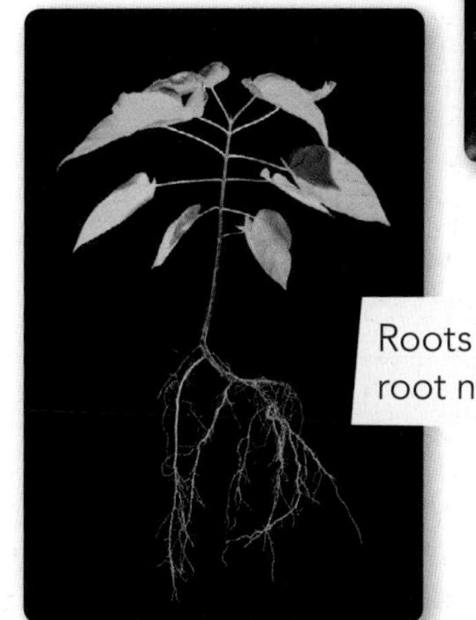

Roots of a plant without root nodules.

QUESTIONS

1. Use your Periodic Table to look up the names of these other essential elements and present the information in a table. The elements are Ca, Mg, S, B, Cl, Fe, Mn and Ni.
2. Why is the essential element which has the symbol Ca needed by a plant? Use the Internet or gardening books to find out.
3. Many plants carry out a vital chemical reaction known as photosynthesis. Find out why plants do this.
4. Write out the word equation for photosynthesis.

Putting something back (how nature does it!)

When plants grow, they remove essential elements from the soil leaving it less fertile. To grow plants in the same soil year after year these essential elements have to be put back. Farmers use natural and artificial **fertilisers** to do this. A fertiliser is a mixture of compounds which contain the essential elements needed by plants. In this chapter we will look at the use of natural methods of putting essential elements back into the soil, including the use of **manure**, **crop rotation** and leguminous plants.

Manure

Manure is a fantastic **natural fertiliser**. The name came from the Middle English word 'manuren' meaning to cultivate land. There are three main types: **compost**, animal manure and plant manure.

Composting – making your own compost

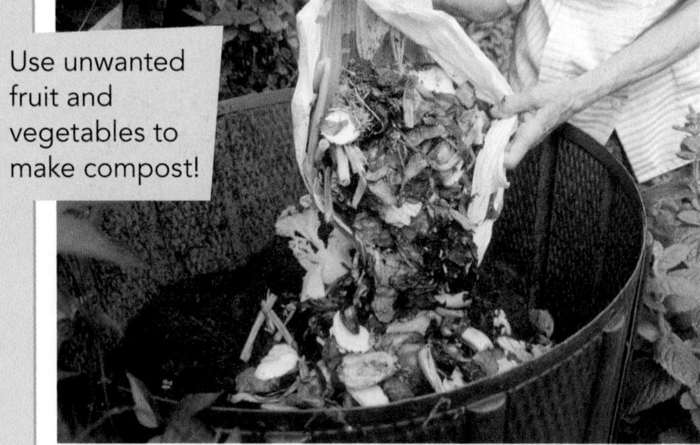

Use unwanted fruit and vegetables to make compost!

If you are keen on recycling you can make your own compost. Compost is mainly made from rotting plant material such as leaves and unwanted fruit and vegetables. The waste material is piled onto a big compost heap or into a compost bin. Then bacteria, fungi, animals and insects which live in soil use oxygen to break down the plant material to make **humus**. Humus is a mixture of soluble compounds which contain the essential elements needed by plants. Composting has been around since time began. Leaves and other plant waste in woodlands and forests have always rotted, returning essential elements to the soil for use by growing plants.

Another way to compost plant material is using a worm composter, which contains special types of worm sometimes known as tiger worms. They are ideal for people with small gardens as they only produce a small amount of liquid compost.

Active Learning

Activities

1 Research one of the following topics:

a) Do a survey of 20 people in your neighbourhood to find out whether they compost food, and if so what they compost. Present your findings in a table or short essay.

b) Does your council supply free compost bins, does it collect composted waste and what kinds of food can be composted? Write a report to present your findings.

c) Make a poster that could be used by your local council to inform people about what can and cannot be put in a compost bin.

2 Make your own wormery to see the composting of plant waste in action.

What a stink!

Animal manure is mainly faeces (poo) and materials such as bedding straw or hay. It is mostly obtained from farm animals, human sewage and **guano** (bird and bat droppings).

A cowpat is a great natural fertiliser.

Animal manures such as human sewage which have a bad smell are injected straight into the soil to reduce the release of the smell. A muck spreader is used to add manure from pigs and cattle to soils. Manure from herbivores such as elephants has very little smell and makes an excellent fertiliser – just go to your nearest zoo to buy some! Using **sewage** to make your flowers grow better is often smelly but sometimes profitable. Professor George Fleming was paid lots of money to take sewage away from Shieldhall sewage works on the banks of the river Clyde. When the organisers of the Glasgow Garden Festival in 1988 realised that he had carted away valuable fertiliser, they paid him to bring it back again.

Hazard warning – large piles of manure can ignite spontaneously (suddenly burst into flames) due to the large amounts of methane gas and heat generated when the waste rots. Methane is a flammable gas so it can catch fire if the temperature gets high enough. In July 2009 in Crawley, England, it took firefighters more than an hour to put out a fire in a pile of manure that was 25 metres long by 10 metres wide.

Manure

Guano makes a great fertiliser due to its high ammonia content. Did you know that droppings from seabirds and bats from Peru are shipped across the Atlantic to the UK? Ammonia (chemical formula NH_3) is soluble in water and contains over 80% nitrogen, so it provides high levels of nitrogen to plants. Guano also contains phosphates (compounds which contain the essential element phosphorus), nitrates (more nitrogen) and other chemicals. It is white in colour and is deposited in huge amounts on sea cliffs in Peru due to the bird population. The dry weather conditions in Peru mean that this soluble material is not washed away by rain.

Many ships built in Port Glasgow, such as the sv Drumcliffe, were used to transport guano around the world. Sailors must have hated shipping this smelly fertiliser. On the long sea voyage the ammonia in the guano made the nostrils of the sailors bleed. Ammonia is a corrosive gas which dissolves in water to form the alkali ammonium hydroxide (see Chapter 11).

Sea cliffs white with guano.

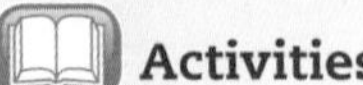

Activities

1 Produce an advert to sell guano to gardeners across Scotland. You can produce a poster, mini movie or cartoon etc.

2 Imagine you are a sailor on a ship carrying a cargo of guano. Send a postcard home describing the conditions on board ship!

3 Guano was used by the Incan civilisations in Peru. Write an essay about the Incan people. You could include information about the lost city of Macchu Picchu and the farming methods used by the Incan people.

Plant manures

Plant manure is also known as green manure. It is usually a leguminous crop which grows quickly. It is then ploughed back into the soil after harvesting. Remember that leguminous plants have nitrifying bacteria which fix nitrogen from the air. When these plants rot, they release soluble nitrogen compounds into soil. This is a cheaper method of fertilising the soil than artificial fertilisers.

Crop rotation

Crop rotation year 1

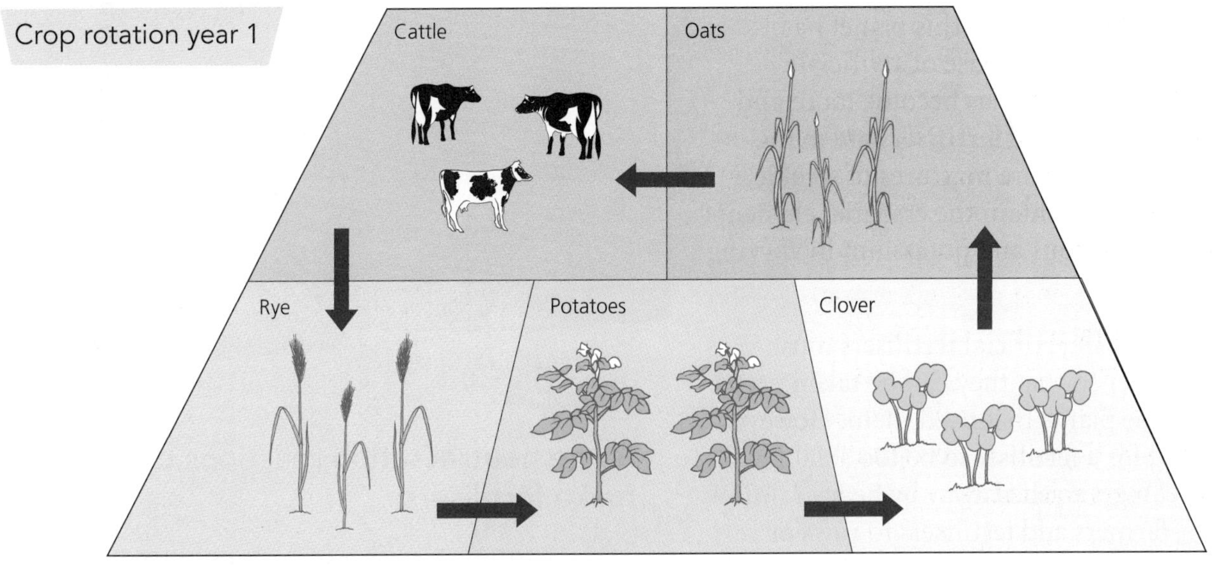

Crop rotation year 2

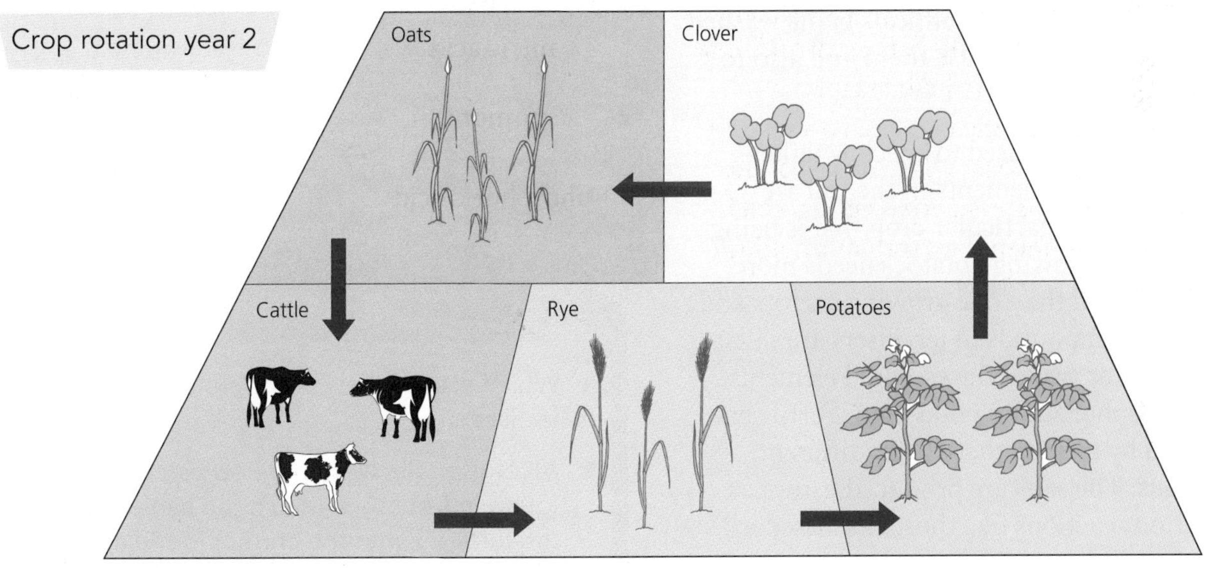

As early as Roman times, around 2000 years ago, crop rotation was used to replace essential elements in soil. In the first year a crop would be grown in a field. The next year green manure such as clover would be grown in the field to put nitrogen compounds back into the soil. This would be followed by a year when the field was used to graze animals, which led to the spreading of animal manure on the land. Today, intensive farming is used make maximum profit from the crops grown on a piece of land. The same crop is grown on the land every year, and it is usual to buy artificial fertilisers to restore the essential elements. Some farmers who are keen to cope without artificial fertilisers use modern crop rotation which involves growing a leguminous plant one year and then a cereal crop such as maize (which is used to make cornflakes) the next.

Artificial fertilisers

As the number of people on this planet has continued to increase, the use of artificial chemicals to grow crops has become more and more popular. **Artificial fertilisers** are man-made fertilisers. They are mixtures of soluble compounds which contain the essential elements nitrogen, phosphorous and potassium in varying amounts.

The compounds in artificial fertilisers must dissolve in water so that they can be taken up by the roots of the plants that need them. However, it is not good for a fertiliser to be too soluble in water as it can get washed away by heavy rainfall. Nowadays, farmers add fertilisers to rows of growing crops at a time when the plants need them to lower the chance of the chemicals being washed away before the plants can use them and also to minimise water pollution.

Soil testing kits can be used to check whether the levels of essential elements in the soil are high enough for the particular crop that is being grown. A farmer growing potatoes needs more nitrogen in the soil than one growing carrots and beetroot. The compounds in fertilisers are salts containing one or two of the essential elements nitrogen, phosphorus and potassium. Fertilisers are produced by mixing the salts in different combinations. The salts are produced using neutralisation reactions like those discussed in Chapter 11.

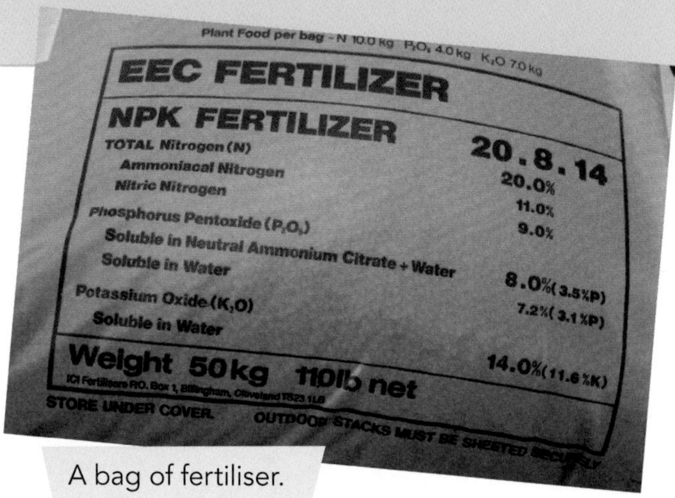

A bag of fertiliser.

Some neutralisation reactions used to make fertilisers:

1 ammonia + nitric acid → ammonium nitrate + water

2 ammonia + phosphoric acid → ammonium phosphate + water

QUESTIONS

1 Which essential elements are found in NPK fertilisers?

2 All of the salts written below can be found in fertilisers. Match the name of the fertiliser with the correct formula, and copy them into your jotter. For example, ammonium nitrate is NH_4NO_3.

Name of the salt	Formula
Ammonium nitrate	$Ca_3(PO_4)_2$
Potassium sulphate	K_2O
Ammonium sulphate	KNO_3
Potassium oxide	NH_4NO_3
Potassium chloride	$(NH_4)_3PO_4$
Calcium phosphate	K_2SO_4
Ammonium phosphate	$(NH_4)_2SO_4$
Potassium nitrate	KCl

Active Learning

Activities

1 Use flame tests to identify the flame colour of compounds containing the essential elements potassium and calcium. Then use flame tests to find out which ones from a variety of different fertilisers provided by your teacher contain these essential elements.

2 Ask your teacher to demonstrate the brown ring test for nitrate salts, and to heat ammonium nitrate salt.

3 Test the solubility of various salts which can be found in fertilisers and make some general conclusions about solubility.

4 Grow pondweed plants in different concentrations of nitrate solution to find out how the essential element nitrogen affects the growth rate of a plant.

5 Use a soil testing kit to look at the pH and the essential elements present in a variety of different soils provided by your teacher.

Pesticides

The growth and quality of a food crop can be severely reduced by plant diseases, pests eating the crop and by weeds competing for soil nutrients. To minimise these effects, chemicals called pesticides are sprayed on crops. As pesticides are usually expensive and can be hazardous to health, they must be used wisely. The main types of pesticide which will be looked at here are insecticides, herbicides and fungicides. Biological control will also be discussed.

Insecticides

Insecticides are used to kill insects such as caterpillars, aphids and black fly. A wide range of insecticides has been developed because insects can cause mass destruction of food crops. They mostly work by killing the insects upon contact or by being absorbed by the plant itself and being taken up by insects when they feed. Many insecticides are toxic to humans and should be washed off fruit and vegetables before they are eaten. There is a range of synthetic and natural insecticides. They can have tremendous benefits but also cause problems. A powerful insecticide called DDT was found to remain in the soil after it had been used to kill insects, and it found its way into the food chain. It was also found to react with other chemicals in the soil, producing even more toxic chemicals. You can find out more about this in *Science for Excellence Level 3: Biological Science*, Chapter 3.

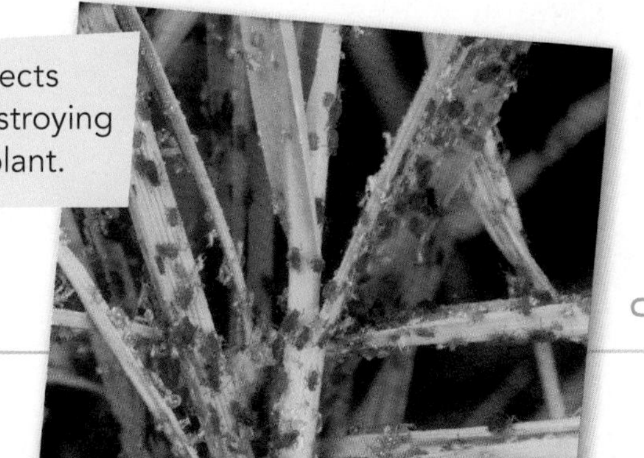

Insects destroying a plant.

Herbicides

Herbicides (weed killers) are used to kill unwanted plants called weeds. Weeds grow quickly and remove essential elements from the soil, leaving less for the crop that is being grown. Weeds sometimes harbour pests such as eelworm which can damage a crop. There is a wide variety of herbicides available. As herbicides are toxic to humans and other animals, they should always be used carefully.

Dandelions are a common weed.

Fungicides

Fungicides are used to control diseases. The element sulphur is a common active ingredient in fungicides. Natural ingredients include rosemary oil, tea tree oil and milk. Milk can be used as an organic fertiliser for certain plants too as it contains potassium, one of the essential elements needed for plant growth.

A diseased tomato plant.

Biological control

Encouraging predators of garden pests can be a good alternative to the use of pesticides. This is called biological control. For example, having a pond in your garden will attract frogs and toads (which eat a variety of insects) to your garden. Hedgehogs like to eat slugs, and can be encouraged to live in your garden by providing a pile of logs for them to shelter under.

Plants can also be useful in protecting crops from pests. This is more practical in a garden where chive, garlic and onion plants can be grown to help keep aphids away and where the herbs rosemary, sage and thyme may guard against caterpillar damage.

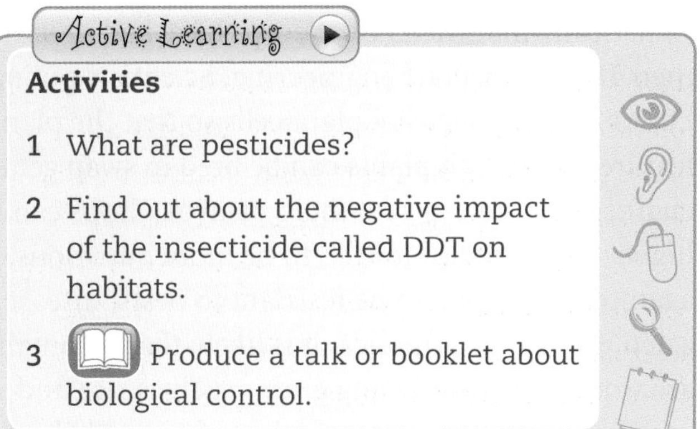

Active Learning

Activities

1. What are pesticides?
2. Find out about the negative impact of the insecticide called DDT on habitats.
3. Produce a talk or booklet about biological control.

Organic farming

The main features of organic farming are that:

- No artificial fertilisers and pesticides are used.
- Modern crop rotation methods and on-farm manures are used to maintain soil fertility. In some instances extra manures can be brought on to the farm.
- Weeds, pests and diseases are controlled without the use of herbicides.

To produce 'organic meat', the animals must graze on land farmed as described above. Strict guidelines set out by the European Union must also be followed by farmers who want to sell organic crops and meat. Shoppers can buy a wide range of organic products nowadays. The price is usually a little higher, reflecting the cost of producing the food in this way.

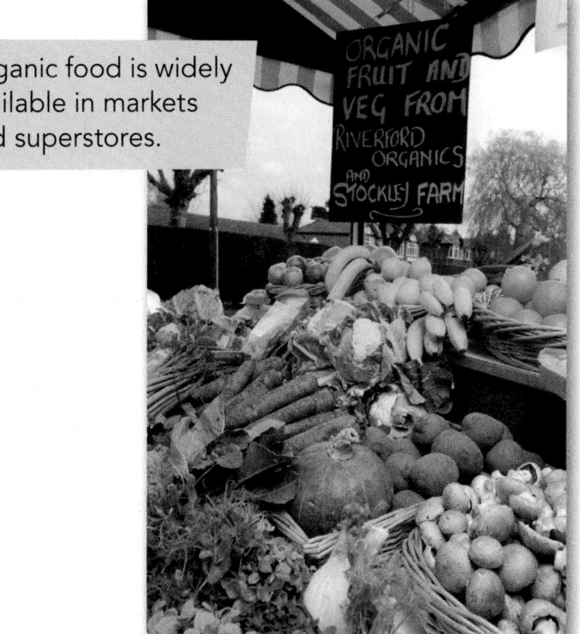

Organic food is widely available in markets and superstores.

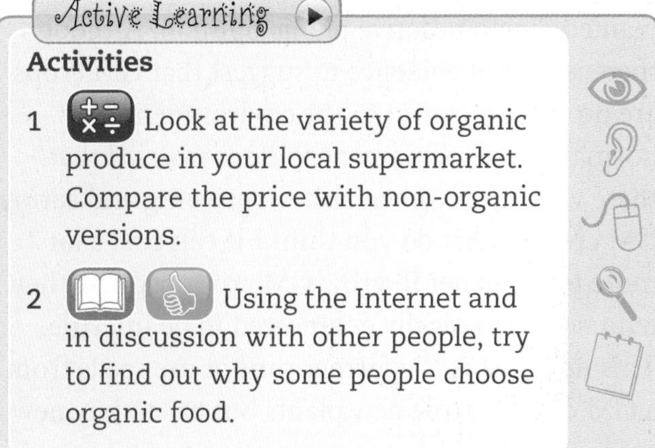

Active Learning

Activities

1. Look at the variety of organic produce in your local supermarket. Compare the price with non-organic versions.
2. Using the Internet and in discussion with other people, try to find out why some people choose organic food.

GM crops

Genetically modified **(GM) crops** have had specific features introduced into their **DNA** by genetic engineering. Scientists put new genes (tiny pieces of DNA) into the nuclei of plant cells so that the plant will inherit these extra features. Although plants can be bred to swap genes naturally, with genetic engineering there is a lot more control. Crops can be engineered to give higher yields, to last longer, to be more nutritious, to give humans resistance against disease and to be resistant to pests, disease, drought etc. If you have eaten a burger in America, it is likely that it contained GM soya. Scientists are working on producing grains such as rice and sorghum which contain more vitamins and other nutrients for people in the world who do not have access to a wide range of foods.

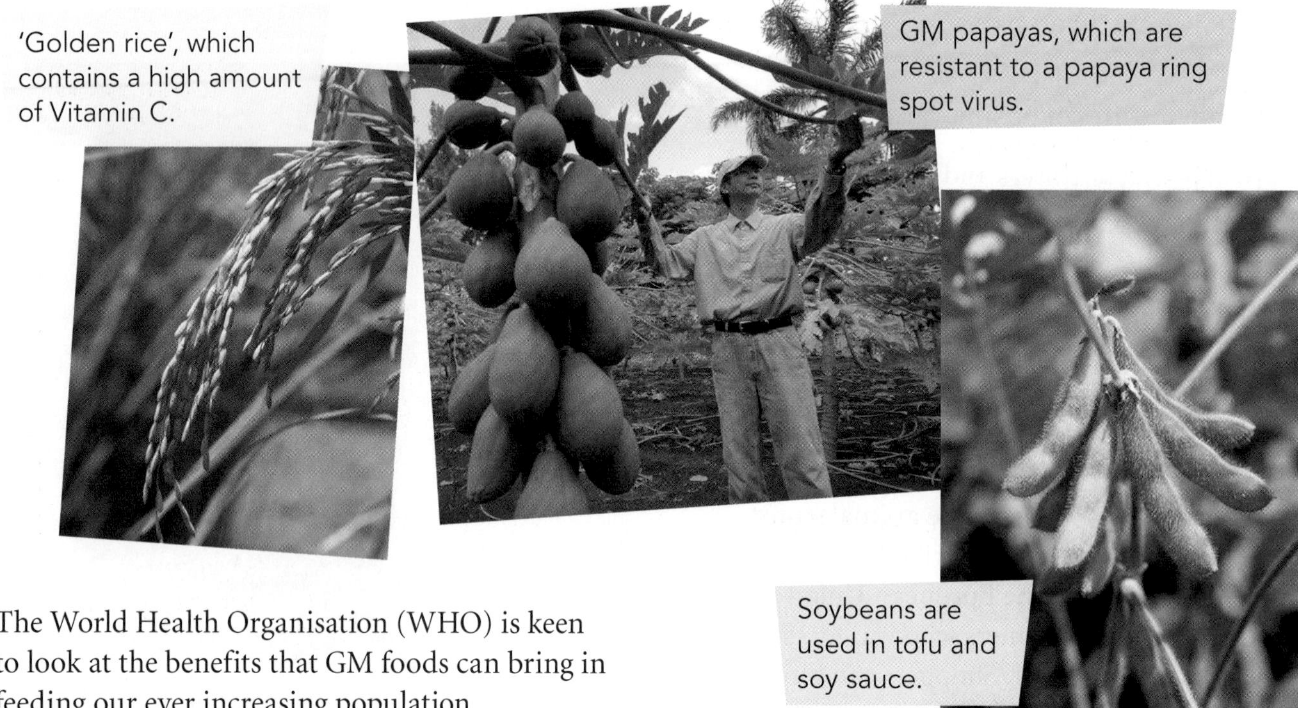

'Golden rice', which contains a high amount of Vitamin C.

GM papayas, which are resistant to a papaya ring spot virus.

Soybeans are used in tofu and soy sauce.

The World Health Organisation (WHO) is keen to look at the benefits that GM foods can bring in feeding our ever increasing population.

However, in Europe very few GM crops have been planted due to negative public opinion. Although there is a lot of evidence to suggest that GM crops are no more harmful to the environment than normal varieties, many people are worried that there will be unknown risks in growing and eating GM crops. What do you think? It can cost a lot more for a farmer to grow GM crops because they tend to be genetically engineered to be infertile. This means that the farmer cannot use seeds from a GM crop to grow new plants but has to buy new seeds every year.

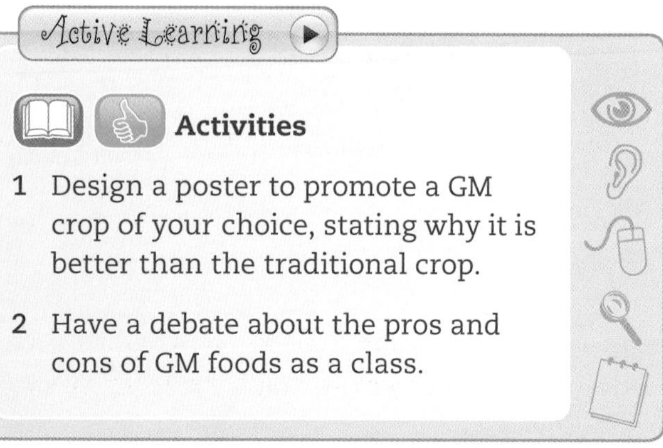

Active Learning

Activities

1 Design a poster to promote a GM crop of your choice, stating why it is better than the traditional crop.

2 Have a debate about the pros and cons of GM foods as a class.

What is polluting our water?

The use of natural and artificial fertilisers and accidental milk spillage from dairies are among the main causes of water pollution in Scotland. They lead to the release of soluble nitrates and phosphates into lochs and rivers which cause **eutrophication**. The presence of pesticides in freshwater is also monitored in the UK but will not be discussed here.

The fact that the nitrates found in fertilisers are soluble in water is both a blessing and a curse. This is great for plants because they are able to absorb these nutrients easily when they take up water from the soil. However, the fact that they are soluble also means that they are easily washed from fields into nearby lochs and rivers. This is more of a problem in the winter months due to the large amount of rainfall in Scotland!

High levels of nitrates in water help aquatic plants like algae and duckweed to grow very quickly. When the surface of lochs and rivers get covered in plants, sunlight and oxygen are prevented from getting through to the plants and fish underneath which need them to survive. The water can often smell and turn red, brown, green or yellow.

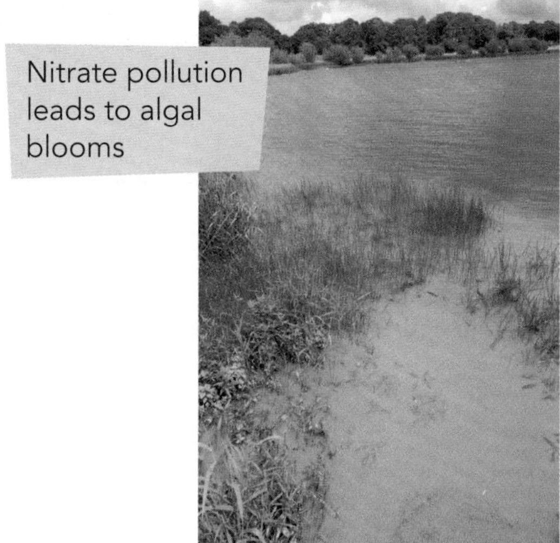

Nitrate pollution leads to algal blooms

Some **algal blooms** are toxic to plants and animals and can work their way through the food chain into humans.

Nitrate pollution is such a problem in some areas of Scotland that nitrate vulnerable zones (NVZs) have been set up. Any farms inside these zones can only apply a limited amount of artificial nitrogen and natural fertilisers to the soil in line with European directives. They cannot apply the fertilisers when the fields are waterlogged, frozen or covered in snow as these types of weather conditions provide a lot of water for washing the nitrates away.

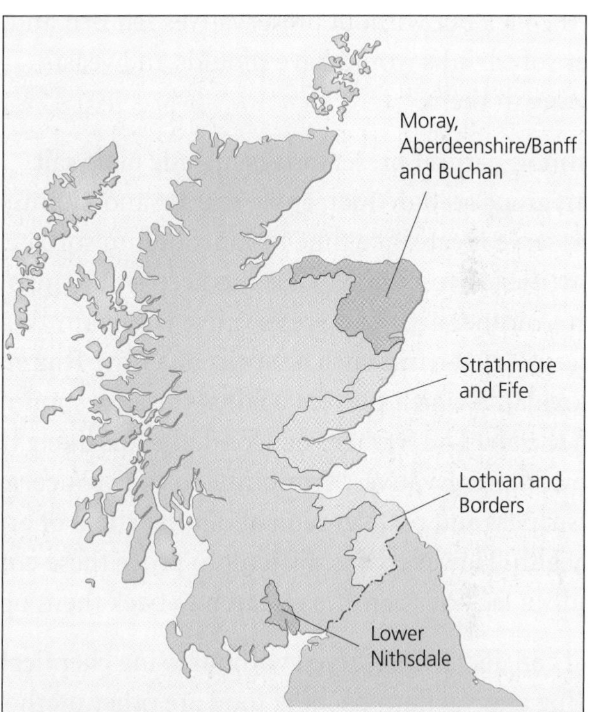

QUESTIONS

1. What is eutrophication?
2. What is a nitrate vulnerable zone?
3. Where are the four nitrate vulnerable zones in Scotland?
4. At what time of year do you think pollution is worst?
5. Ask your teacher to show you how to investigate the effect of nitrate concentration on the growth of algae bloom.

Food preservatives – check out the label!

Food preservatives are chemicals which are added to foods to make them last longer. The chemicals are compounds which can be natural or synthetic. They usually work by stopping micro-organisms from spoiling the food. In Europe, any preservative added to food, even if it is natural, is given an E-number. The 'E' stands for 'Europe'. E200–E299 are preservatives. Apart from the food grown in your own garden, it is likely that most of the food that you eat has been treated with preservatives. You may not like the idea but without preservatives Irn Bru and other soft drinks would have moulds and yeasts growing in them.

Milk chocolate (70%) in a crisp coloured shell • Ingredients: sugar, cocoa mass, skimmed milk powder, lactose and milk proteins, cocoa butter, milk fat, vegetable fat, glucose syrup, starch, emulsifier (soya lecithin), colours (E100, E120, E133, E160e, E171), dextrin, glazing agent (carnauba wax), flavourings, salt, vegetable oil. (Traces: peanut, hazelnut, almond). Milk chocolate contains milk solids 14% minimum.
™/®/designs/© Mars
Best before: see base
Milk chocolate contains vegetable fats in addition to cocoa butter.
To avoid suffocation, keep bags away from babies, young children and pets.

How many E-numbers are there in these chocolate sweets?

Common natural preservatives include table salt, sugar, grape seed extract, apple extract and vitamin C. Salt has been used to preserve meat since time began. Sodium sorbate and sodium benzoate are artificial preservatives used to keep soft drinks and tomato ketchup fresh. Another artificial preservative is sulphur dioxide which is used to preserve dried fruits such as apricots. Other E-numbers added to food are antioxidants which prevent against the slow spoiling of food by reaction with the air. The fresher your food, the less likely that food will contain chemical preservatives. From time to time concerns are expressed in the newspapers and on television about the effect of artificial preservatives on health. However, it is difficult to prove these concerns as there is usually a lack of scientific research to back them up.

Food can also be preserved without using chemicals – UV radiation, heating and vacuum packing food are other methods which are widely used.

Active Learning

Activities

1 Look at the labels of some of your favourite foods to see which preservatives are used.

2 Write a letter to a friend who is worried about giving food containing E-numbers to her children.

3 Find out the name and use of these E-numbers:

a) E100, b) E175, c) E210, d) E300, e) E355, f) E406, g) E621 and h) E938.

4 Who discovered that vitamin C was an antioxidant that could be used as a preservative in bread and beer?

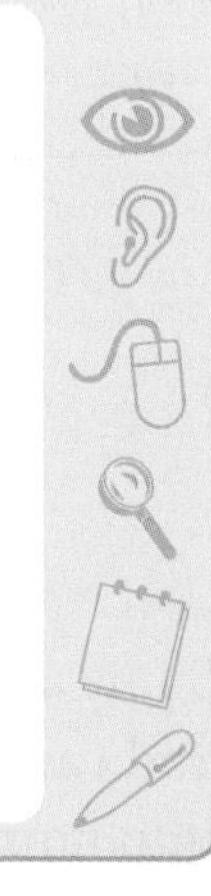

Newspaper project: co-operative learning activity

Academic Task – in groups of four produce a newspaper or magazine to discuss the importance of science in growing food crops.

The name of the newspaper or magazine and layout of the front cover should be decided by the group and roles and articles should be decided at the start.

Social task – to work as a team with all pupils contributing.

Roles – each person in your group should have one of the following roles:

Editor

Photographer/Artist

Layout manager

Materials manager

Articles – each person in your group should be responsible for at least one of the following articles:

A country experiencing starvation due to an inability to grow enough crops to feed its own people.

Information about a crop that grows well in Scotland and why.

Information about the use of fertilisers in crop production

Information about GM crops

A puzzle page/Cartoon/Adverts

GLOSSARY

Algal bloom a heavy growth of algae in and on an area of water

Artificial fertilisers fertilisers made by chemical industry

Bioethanol a fuel made from plant materials using a fermentation reaction

Compost a natural fertiliser made from rotting plant material

Crop rotation where a field is used to grow crops one year, to graze animals the following year and to grow leguminous plants like clover the year after that to maintain soil fertility

DNA deoxyribonucleic acid

Essential element an element which is essential for healthy plant growth

Eutrophication a process in which the concentration of nutrients in an area of water increases, leading to algal blooms which lower the levels of oxygen and light needed for underwater life

Fertiliser a substance which is used to improve soil fertility; a source of essential elements

Food preservatives chemicals added to food to make them last longer

GM crops genetically modified crops

Guano bird or bat droppings; a natural fertiliser

Leguminous a type of plant which has root nodules containing nitrifying bacteria

Manure any natural compost

Natural fertilisers fertilisers made directly from animal or plant waste

Nitrifying bacteria bacteria which can change nitrogen from the air into soluble nitrogen compounds

Sewage water carrying waste from toilets, sinks and so on

MATERIALS

Chemical Changes

11

pH

Level 2 What came before?

 **SCN 2-18a**

I have investigated different water samples from the environment and explored methods that can be used to clean and conserve water and I am aware of the properties and uses of water.

Level 3 What is this chapter about?

 **SCN 3-18a**

Having taken part in practical activities to compare the properties of acids and bases, I have demonstrated ways of measuring and adjusting pH and can describe the significance of pH in everyday life.

pH

What are acids and alkalis?

Many everyday substances that we use can be classified as **acids** or **alkalis**; for example, milk is actually an acid! The chemical opposite of an acid is an alkali and many of the products you find in cupboards at home are acidic or alkaline.

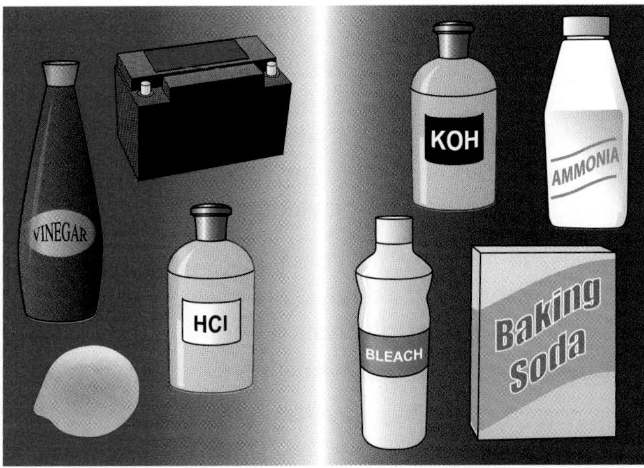

Drinking milk is not dangerous, but drinking a lab acid like hydrochloric acid could be fatal. This is because hydrochloric acid is more acidic than milk. We measure acidity and alkalinity using the **pH** scale. Part of the pH scale is shown below.

Acidic substances have a pH of less than 7. The most acidic substances have a pH of 1 and acidity decreases as the pH number increases from 1 to 7. Some of the acids which you will come across in the lab have a low pH of 1–3. Some of the acids which you will come across outside the lab, such as vinegar, orange juice and lemon juice will have a higher pH of 4–6. Even rain water is weakly acidic.

What other everyday acids do you know of?

A selection of household acids.

If a substance is neither an acid nor an alkali, it is **neutral** and has a pH value of exactly 7. Pure water is an example of a neutral substance.

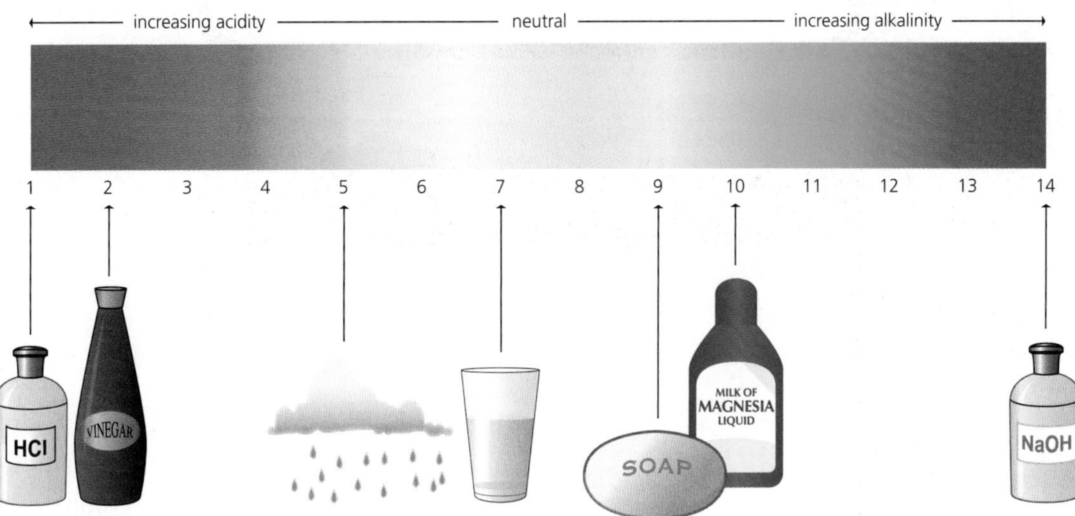

What are acids and alkalis?

Alkalis have pH greater than 7. The higher the pH the more alkaline a substance is. Alkalis are commonly used as cleaning products and indigestion remedies.

A selection of household alkalis.

QUESTIONS

1 Draw a table with three columns titled 'Acid', 'Alkali' and 'Neutral'. Fill in the table using all the substances mentioned on the previous page.

Acid	Alkali	Neutral

2 Why do you think that hydrochloric acid in the lab has a warning label on it, but a bottle of vinegar does not?

3 Have a look at the food and drinks in your cupboards at home. Make a list of which items have acidic ingredients.

Indicators

What are **indicators**? In a car, the indicators are lights that flash to show pedestrians and other drivers which way the car is going to turn. In the lab, indicators are chemicals that change colour to give information about a substance. Simple pH indicators such as litmus will show if a substance is acidic or alkaline. Litmus is normally used as a purple solution. When added to an acid, litmus turns red. When added to an alkali it turns blue.

However, using litmus does not tell us **how** acidic or alkaline a substance is. To find this out we must use a different indicator. Universal indicator is one of the most useful indicators because it turns a different colour for every pH value.

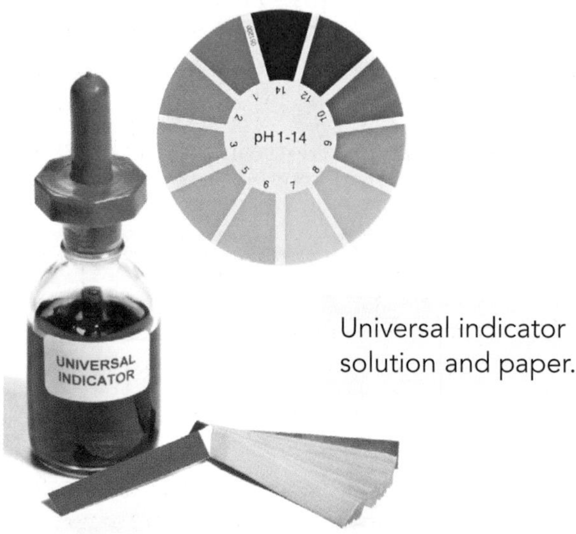

Universal indicator solution and paper.

Universal indicator is available as pH paper strips or as a solution. When pH paper touches the liquid you want to test, it will change colour.

Indicators

Universal indicator solution is also widely used. To use a pH indicator such as universal indicator, simply add it to the solution you want to test and compare the colour to a standard colour chart. Adding a few drops of universal indicator to some hydrochloric acid could result in the red colour that corresponds to pH 1.

Not all indicators are complicated chemicals that you find in science labs. You can even make your own indicator in a school lab or at home using red cabbage or another brightly coloured vegetable (**see the Activity** on page 152). Plants such as hydrangeas even work as indicators while they are growing! A hydrangea will change colour depending on the pH of the soil that it is planted in. Most species of hydrangea have white flowers, but these can be blue in acidic soil conditions, cream under neutral conditions and pink or purple when the soil is alkaline.

QUESTIONS

1 In your own words, describe why pH indicators are useful chemicals.

2 What colour would universal indicator turn if pure water was added to it? What colour would it turn if rain water was used instead of pure water? You could even try this at home or in the lab. Collect some rain water and test its pH to see if it is different to distilled water in the lab.

3 Draw a full colour pH scale like the one on page 149. Show on your pH scale where the following substances would be: sodium hydroxide, soap, vinegar, hydrochloric acid. Your teacher might let you make a poster of this.

Active Learning

Activities

1 a) Get some red cabbage leaves, cut them into small pieces and then grind them up using a mortar and pestle.

b) Next, add a little methylated spirits to the crushed plant material. This will help to extract the colour that you will use as the indicator. Continue to crush the mixture until all the colour has come out.

c) To use your indicator, remove some of the liquid using a **pipette**. Add it to some substances whose pH you already know. Try to make a red cabbage indicator colour chart which matches the colours to pH values.

2

The mechanic has spilled some battery acid while checking the power of the battery. He immediately pours water on the spilled acid. Does adding water help? Will it change the acid's pH making it less acidic? Can we change the pH of a substance? Think about this problem. What is your hypothesis? Design an experiment which would answer those questions. What equipment will you need?

3 Do you think alkalis will behave similarly? What about neutral solutions? Design further experiments to find out.

Neutralisation

At the start of this chapter, we learned that acids and alkalis are chemical opposites. What do you think would happen if an acid and an alkali were mixed together? We could follow the reaction by adding an indicator and noting any colour change.

The acid and alkali will react together to form new products in a **neutralisation** reaction. Whenever an acid and alkali react together, the same two products will always be formed; a salt and water.

The word equation for this neutralisation reaction is shown below:

Acid + Alkali $\rightarrow$ Salt + Water

This is called a neutralisation reaction because the water which is produced is neutral.

If an alkali is added to a solution of an acid, the pH would move up towards 7. Similarly, if an acid is added to an alkali the pH value would move down towards 7.

Neutralisation can be a very useful reaction. Do you know what to do if you are stung by a bee? When a bee stings you, it is actually injecting an acid (methanoic acid) into your skin. You can neutralise the sting by washing the affected area with baking soda (a common household chemical which can neutralise acids). Similarly, a wasp sting is alkaline, so an acid like vinegar or lemon juice should be applied to soothe the area.If you added an acid to a bee sting or an alkali to a wasp sting it would hurt more, so try to remember which is which!

Neutralisation

If you have eaten too quickly and have a sore stomach, you need to be neutralised! There is acid in your stomach to help digest food. Indigestion is caused by a build up of this acid when you eat too quickly. Indigestion tablets contain alkalis like calcium carbonate and sodium hydrogen carbonate. These alkalis will neutralise the acid that has built up. Many restaurants offer a selection of cheeses as a dessert after a main course. Eating cheese which is slightly alkaline helps to neutralise acid in the mouth and protect tooth enamel.

It is not just humans who need a balanced pH to live happily – plants do too. Certain plants grow well in acidic soil whereas some plants grow well in neutral soil and others still in alkaline soil. Chemicals can be added to the soil to make the pH an ideal match for the plant you are trying to grow too.

Fish are also fussy. If the water they live in is too acidic, then the fish will not survive. The pH of tropical fish tanks can be tested at home with test kits to make sure the fish are healthy and happy. This is not as easy in nature but large lochs can have their pH adjusted by adding large chunks of limestone if the water is found to be too acidic.

Testing the pH of a soil sample.

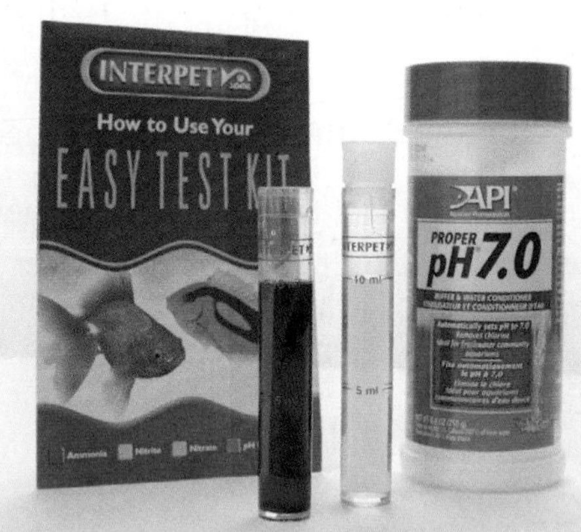

A home pH test kit for a tropical fish tank.

QUESTIONS

1 A lab technician is working with some chemicals and accidentally spills some concentrated sulphuric acid on the floor. Describe how she could safely clean up the mess.

2 What happens to the pH of:

a) an acid, and

b) an alkali when it is neutralised?

3 Give three examples of everyday neutralisation.

4 Find out how the fire service deals with a large scale spillage of acid, say from a transporter lorry which has crashed.

Active Learning

Activity

Find out about the chemical called bicarbonate of soda. What is it normally used for at home? What else might it be used for? Write an advert for bicarbonate of soda, the wonder chemical.

Acid rain

You have probably heard of the **acid rain** pollution problem, but what causes acid rain? What are the effects of it? Earlier in this chapter you may have tested rain water and found that it is naturally acidic. Could this be dangerous to us?

Rain water is naturally acidic because carbon dioxide in the air is slightly soluble in water, forming carbonic acid:

Carbon Dioxide + Water → Carbonic Acid.

The pH of unpolluted rain water is only slightly less than 7, so it is not harmful to us. Acid rain will not burn us either if it lands on us, but it does have a very serious effect on other living things. It may take years, but acid rain can cause all of the plants and animals in rivers, streams and lakes to die. It also causes damage to certain types of stone and metal over long periods. So what exactly is acid rain?

Carbon dioxide is not the only gas which dissolves in water. Other gases can also dissolve, making the rain water even more acidic with a much lower pH. When this happens, the rail is called acid rain. So what are these gases, and how do they get into the air? There are two answers to this.

Acid rain

Sulphur dioxide

Sulphur is present as an impurity in fossil fuels, especially coal. When coal is burned in power stations to provide us with electricity, the sulphur impurities are also burned and form sulphur dioxide gas. In the atmosphere, sulphur dioxide reacts with water to produce sulphuric acid.

Compounds containing sulphur are present in North Sea oil as impurities. Petrol and diesel fuel are made from this oil (see Chapter 8), and so these fuels are also contaminated with compounds containing sulphur. It would be very expensive to remove these compounds, so we don't. Look at the pumps next time you are in a petrol station – they sell **low sulphur** petrol and **low sulphur** diesel. However, low sulphur does not mean no sulphur. The result of this is that as well as burning the fuel we also burn the sulphur. What is the result of this? More sulphur dioxide and more sulphuric acid – acid rain.

Sulphur dioxide is also released into the atmosphere naturally from volcanoes. This leads to acid rain too.

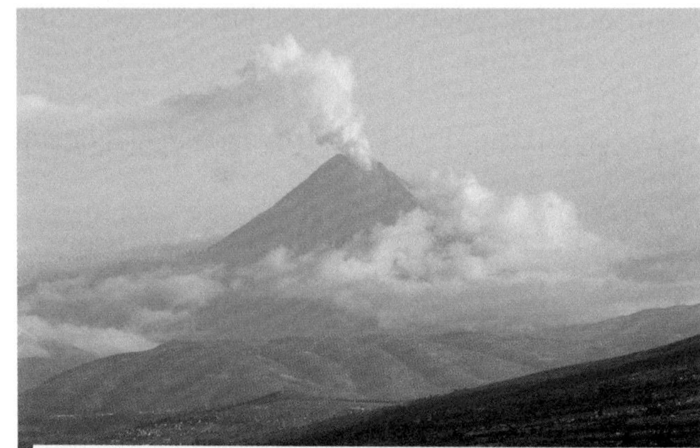

Tungurahua volcano erupting in Ecuador in 2007. Lots of gases are produced when a volcano erupts, including sulphur dioxide.

Nitrogen dioxide

Motor cars with petrol engines use **spark plugs** to **ignite** the petrol.

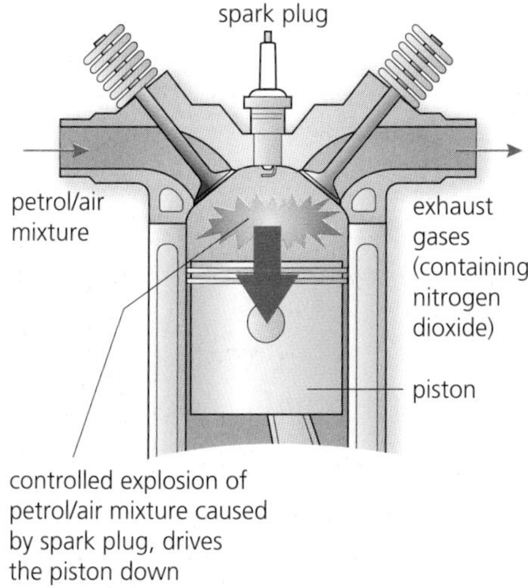

The high energy in these sparks also causes nitrogen and oxygen present in air to react with each other:

Nitrogen + Oxygen → Nitrogen Monoxide

This nitrogen monoxide then immediately reacts with more oxygen:

Nitrogen Monoxide + Oxygen → Nitrogen Dioxide

Nitrogen dioxide, more oxygen and water then combine to form nitric acid:

Nitrogen Dioxide + Oxygen + Water → Nitric Acid

As mentioned earlier, acid rain is a problem because it damages our environment. It can lower the pH of lochs which can cause fish to die. The pH of soil can be lowered which prevents plants from growing, and the leaves of trees can be damaged by acid rain. This can be a real problem in Scotland as our many lochs also receive A LOT of rainfall. The pH of Loch Dee in Galloway has been monitored for nearly 30 years now to track changes caused by pollution.

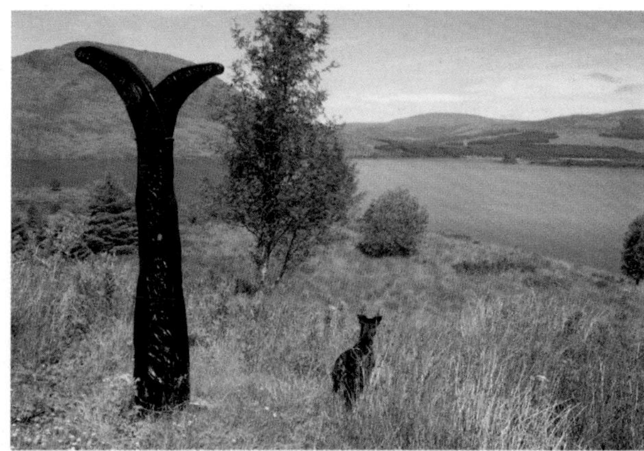

Acid rain also reacts with buildings made from limestone and marble, eroding their features. However, it's not just stone structures that are at risk; structures such as bridges made from steel rust more quickly when they are exposed to acid rain.

Damage caused by acid rain.

QUESTIONS

1 Name two gases which can cause acid rain. How are they released into our environment?

2 Petrol engines are also responsible for reacting nitrogen with oxygen. Name the soluble acidic gas that is produced by combustion in petrol engines.

3 Make a list of some of the problems caused by acid rain.

Preventing acid rain

In power stations, chemical scrubbers are currently used to remove sulphur dioxide before it enters our atmosphere. This is expensive. Also, car exhausts are fitted with **catalytic converters**. These change acidic and poisonous gases produced in car engines into less harmful gases; however, they are also expensive.

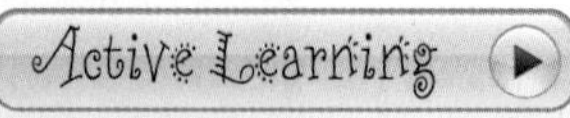

Activities

1 What else could we do? Two simple solutions would be to:

- stop burning fossil fuels in power stations – find **alternative** ways of making electricity.
- stop using vehicles which burn petrol and diesel fuel – develop **alternative** forms of transport.

Each solution includes the word **alternative**. What does this mean? Try to find out what the possibilities are in each case and write an article for your local newspaper based on your research.

2 Most local authorities in Scotland have air pollution monitoring systems. Find out about the levels of sulphur dioxide and nitrogen dioxide pollution in your nearest town or city. Present your findings as a graph or chart.

3 Find out which countries suffer most from acid rain and what they are doing about it.

Salts

Earlier in this chapter we learned that when an acid is neutralised by an alkali, two products are formed – a salt and water:

$$\text{Acid} + \text{Alkali} \rightarrow \text{Salt} + \text{Water}$$

When you think of salt, you are probably thinking of table salt, which is a chemical called sodium chloride. Do you know which elements it contains?

Salts

To a chemist, this is only one of a whole range of salts which can be made by neutralising acids. The salt formed depends on which acid and alkali have been used in the neutralisation reaction. Sodium chloride is readily mined or obtained from sea water but can also be made in the lab by a neutralisation reaction.

The word equation is shown below:

Hydrochloric Acid + Sodium Hydroxide → Sodium Chloride + Water

There are two parts to a salt's name, in the same way that there are two parts to your name. The last part of this one (the surname or family name) is chloride. This has come from hydrochloric acid. Your surname or family name will be the same as your parent or guardian's and it is the same for the salt and the 'parent' acid. The endings for salt names are shown in this table.

Name of acid	Salt name ends with...
Hydrochloric acid	...chloride
Sulphuric acid	...sulphate
Nitric acid	...nitrate

The salt's first name comes from the metal part of the alkali (the first name of the alkali). Some examples are shown in this table.

Name of alkali	Salt name starts with...
Sodium hydroxide	Sodium...
Potassium hydroxide	Potassium...
Magnesium hydroxide	Magnesium...

So in a neutralisation reaction between sulphuric acid and potassium hydroxide, the products would be potassium sulphate and water. This can be represented by the following word equation:

Sulphuric Acid + Potassium Hydroxide → Potassium Sulphate + Water

QUESTIONS

Copy and complete the following word equations (remember to name the salt correctly):

a) Nitric Acid + Magnesium Hydroxide → _______ + _______.

b) Hydrochloric Acid + Potassium Hydroxide → _______ + _______.

c) Sodium Hydroxide + Sulphuric Acid → _______ + _______.

d) Hydrochloric Acid + ___________ → Calcium Chloride + _______.

Active Learning

Activities

1 When a salt is made in the lab, water is also formed. Often a salt **solution** is produced because the salt is soluble in water. Describe how the water could be removed to leave a sample of the solid salt. Draw a labelled diagram of the apparatus required.

2 Sometimes the salt formed is insoluble in water. Again, describe how you could separate the salt from the water, and draw a labelled diagram to illustrate this.

3 Some pupils want to react hydrochloric acid with sodium hydroxide to make table salt.

a) What equipment would they need?

b) Describe how they should carry out this experiment safely.

c) Apart from the salt, what else would be formed?

d) What is the pH of this other product?

Ask your teacher if you can try this experiment.

Neutralisation again

Alkalis are not the only chemicals which can neutralise acids. Metal carbonate compounds also neutralise acids, producing three products.

Acid + Metal Carbonate → Salt + Water + Carbon Dioxide

As you can see, as well as a salt and water, carbon dioxide gas is also produced by this reaction. If we carry out the reaction in the lab, we should observe bubbles of a gas being given off (**effervescence**).

Calcium carbonate reacts with dilute hydrochloric acid to produce carbon dioxide.

How do we know that these are bubbles of carbon dioxide gas? We would need to test the gas that is produced. An experiment like the one opposite could be set up. Here, any gas produced by the reaction will bubble through the solution of lime water. Lime water is a colourless solution, but in the presence of carbon dioxide it will turn to a cloudy white colour.

The chemical test for carbon dioxide is that it turns lime water from colourless to cloudy white.

Naming the salt that is produced when an acid is neutralised by a metal carbonate is easy if you follow the rules we learned previously. The 'parent' acid still gives the salt its surname or family name, and the first name is the metal of the metal carbonate. Which salt would be produced when calcium carbonate neutralises hydrochloric acid?

Acid rain and carbonates

Limestone is a natural material that is mainly made up of calcium carbonate. It is an important building material that was mined for many years in Scotland at Bannockburn, south of Stirling. Limestone was also used as a building material for many famous structures including the Great Pyramid of Giza in Egypt. Over time limestone will erode due to the weather. This erosion is made worse by acid rain.

A limestone mine.

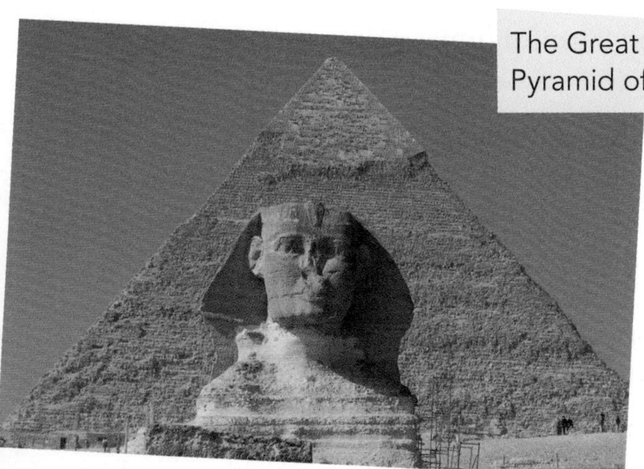

The Great Pyramid of Giza.

QUESTIONS

1 Ben and James are adding lumps of calcium carbonate to a solution of sulphuric acid.

a) Suggest a pH for the acid they are using.

b) Write the word equation for the reaction, correctly naming all the products.

c) How could they identify the gas produced?

2 a) Make a list of reasons why you think limestone was widely used as a building material in the late 1800s and early 1900s.

b) Why do you think limestone is not as popular as a building material now?

GLOSSARY

Acid a substance which has a pH of less than 7

Acid Rain a pollution problem caused by soluble acidic gases dissolving in our atmosphere and acidifying rain water

Alkali a substance which has a pH greater than 7

Catalytic Converter part of a car's exhaust used to cut down on harmful fumes being emitted

Efferevesence the formation of bubbles of a gas from a liquid during a chemical reaction

Indicators chemicals which change colour to tell you something about a substance

Neutral a substance that is neither acidic nor alkaline and has a pH of exactly 7

Neutralisation a type of chemical reaction in which the pH moves towards 7

pH a number used to measure how acidic or alkaline a substance is

Pipette a piece of glass or plastic lab equipment used to transfer measured volumes of a liquid or solution

PLANET EARTH

Processes of the Planet

12 COPs and robbers

Level 2 What came before?

 **SCN 2-05a**

I can apply my knowledge of how water changes state to help me understand the processes involved in the water cycle in nature over time.

Level 3 What is this chapter about?

 **SCN 3-05b**

I can explain some of the processes which contribute to climate change and discuss the possible impact of atmospheric change on the survival of living things.

COPs and robbers

An ice sculpture of a polar bear outside the conference centre in Copenhagen, 2009.

In 1995 the city of Berlin hosted the first United Nations Climate Change Conference. Known as COP1 (Conference of the Parties Number 1), this resulted in 'The Berlin Mandate', which set a 2-year period during which each country should analyse and evaluate its current position in terms of greenhouse gas emissions. The idea was that member countries could come up with solutions to their own problems. There has been a conference every year since then (actually there were two in 2001), each hosted by a different city and it has become clear that countries cannot look at the problem in isolation – it is a global issue where what happens in one country can affect others. At COP15 in Copenhagen in 2009, a life-sized sculpture of a polar bear was created using ice, and placed outside the conference centre.

People were able to touch it, and during the 2 weeks of the conference the bear melted, leaving behind only a bronze skeleton and a large pool of water. This illustrated two powerful environmental messages – polar bears are an endangered species and water from melting Polar ice caps can cause problems. So are future generations being robbed? This chapter will look at some of the science behind climate change and will help you to understand some of the main issues.

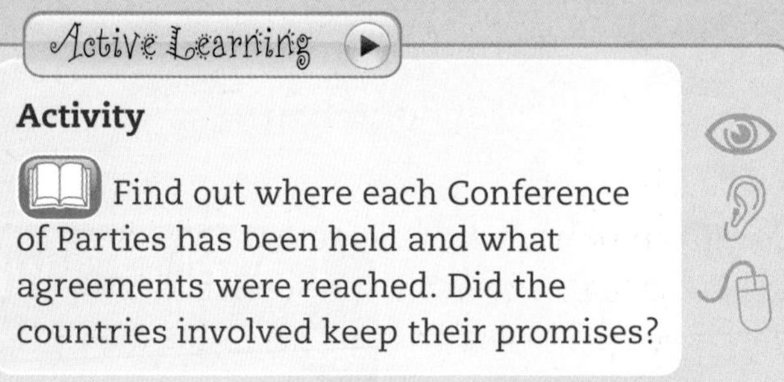

Activity

Find out where each Conference of Parties has been held and what agreements were reached. Did the countries involved keep their promises?

Climate change

Much has been written and said about climate change in newspapers and on television. It is important not to become confused over three of the main issues. These are **global warming**, **ozone depletion** and **acid rain**. The acid rain problem is explored in Chapter 11.

Global warming

People in countries such as Scotland often wish for warmer summers and milder winters, so why all the fuss about global warming? Well it's to do with the meaning of the word 'global'. You cannot simply consider Scotland or any other country in isolation. The whole planet could be affected, so what's good for Scotland could be disastrous elsewhere. In some countries, the weather may become more pleasant, crops may grow better and fewer old people may die during the milder winters. At the same time, other countries may experience floods and crop failures. So in order to be able to form an opinion it is necessary to understand what causes global warming, and how scientists make their predictions about its effects.

Climate change

Greenhouse gases and the Greenhouse Effect

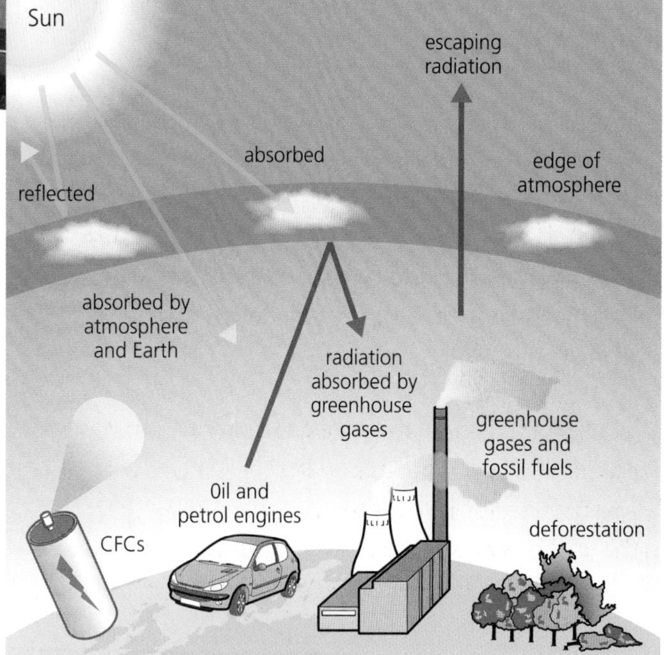

Do you know what a greenhouse is and what it does? A greenhouse is like a garden shed built of glass. Keen gardeners grow plants inside them; plants which need warm conditions to grow. Greenhouses are warm all the time because the glass traps some of the daytime heat from the Sun, meaning that greenhouses stay warm at night when the Sun does not shine. Planet Earth behaves like a giant greenhouse, warming up during the day and cooling down at night, but not too much. But what is the 'glass covering' over the Earth? It's our atmosphere. In a previous chapter of this book ('Pure as snow') you learned about some of the gases of the atmosphere – nitrogen, oxygen, helium, neon, argon, krypton, xenon, radon, water vapour and carbon dioxide. During the day these gases allow enough heat from the Sun to reach Earth to allow life to survive. At night these gases also stop some of this heat escaping. This is known as the **Greenhouse Effect**, and without it planet Earth would be incredibly hot during the day and incredibly cold during the night. There would be no life on Earth!

Active Learning

Activity

The Moon does not have an atmosphere like ours, and so there can be huge changes in temperature there. Try to find out just how cold and how hot it can get on the Moon. Investigate the temperatures on Mars too.

Climate change

The Earth's atmosphere should contain a constant level of about 0.03% carbon dioxide, because a natural process which uses up carbon dioxide, **photosynthesis**, is balanced by another one which produces it, **respiration.** (See *Science for Excellence Level 3: Biological Science.*)

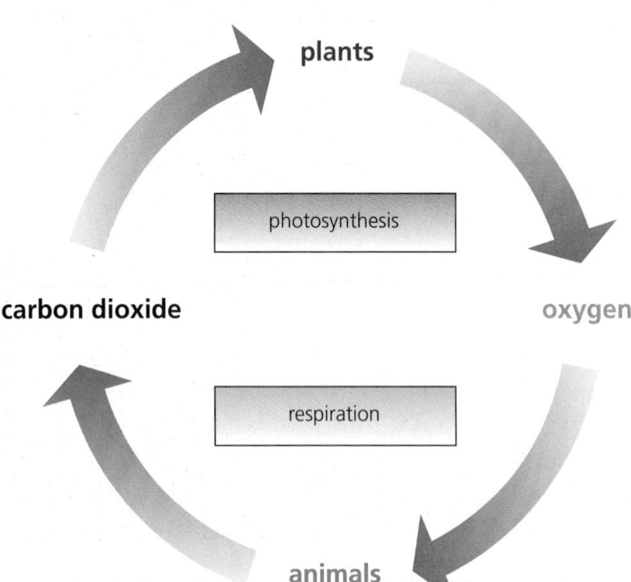

However, in the late twentieth century scientists observed that carbon dioxide levels in the atmosphere were rising.

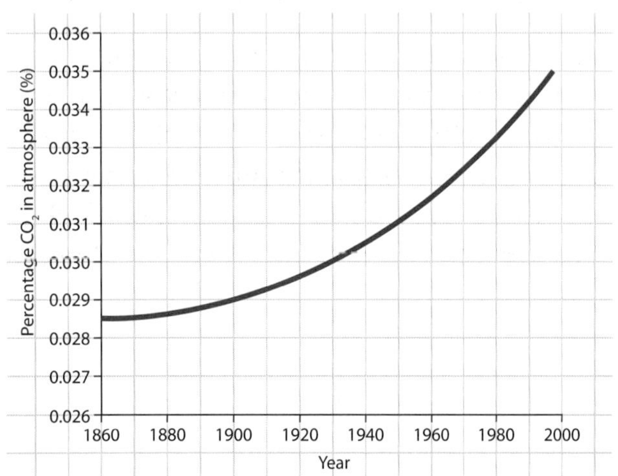

They also claimed to have established a clear link between this fact and a rise in the average temperature of the planet. This is known as global warming.

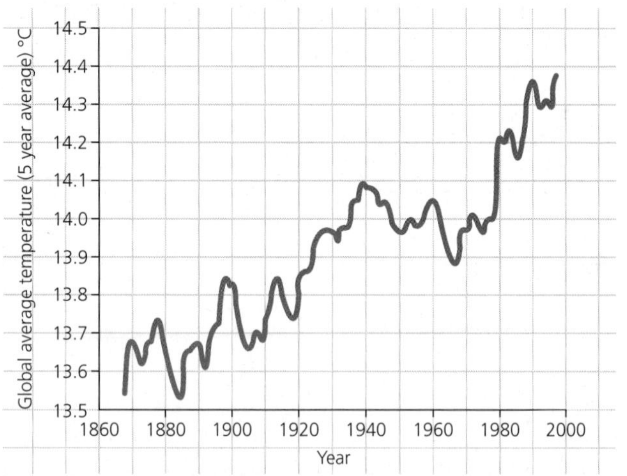

What do you notice when you look at these two graphs? As carbon dioxide levels in the atmosphere have risen, so has the average temperature on our planet. Some people believe that this extra carbon dioxide is what has caused global warming, and carbon dioxide has become widely known as 'the greenhouse gas'. However, scientists have identified other gases in the atmosphere which also contribute to global warming, but this chapter will concentrate on carbon dioxide.

Active Learning

Activity

Carbon dioxide is not the only greenhouse gas (that is, a gas which can cause the Earth's temperature to rise if too much of it gets into our atmosphere), and it is not the worst greenhouse gas. Try to find out the names of other greenhouse gases – draw a table which lists them in order of their ability to cause global warming starting with the most damaging to our atmosphere, and include in the table the source(s) of these other greenhouse gases.

Why are levels rising?

There are two reasons, and together they produce a 'double whammy'. First, there is deforestation – cutting down forests of trees around the world which use up carbon dioxide during photosynthesis.

Creating a desert in an oasis?

Second, there is the burning of fossil fuels. Burning is a chemical reaction in which a substance reacts with oxygen. When substances burn, the products of the reaction are chemicals called oxides – an **oxide** is a compound made from another element and oxygen. One of the main sources of extra carbon dioxide in the air is coal-fired power stations. Coal is made almost entirely of carbon, so when it is burned, it produces carbon dioxide:

Carbon + Oxygen → Carbon Dioxide

The chimneys of these power stations have dumped enormous quantities of this gas into our atmosphere during the last century. Many modern power stations do not burn coal – they burn natural gas or oil. However, this has not solved the problem of extra carbon dioxide in the air, because natural gas and oil are **hydrocarbons** – compounds made of hydrogen and carbon only. When burned, they produce the oxide of hydrogen, which is simply water and the oxide of carbon – carbon dioxide! For example, natural gas is a hydrocarbon called methane, whose chemical formula is CH_4. When methane is burned, the following chemical reaction takes place:

Methane + Oxygen → Carbon dioxide + Water

Natural gas is also used to heat homes and cook food. The petrol and diesel used in motor vehicles are also hydrocarbons, so every car, taxi, bus, lorry and aeroplane is adding to the problem. Houses, factories, offices and schools with gas or oil-fired heating systems also produce lots of carbon dioxide.

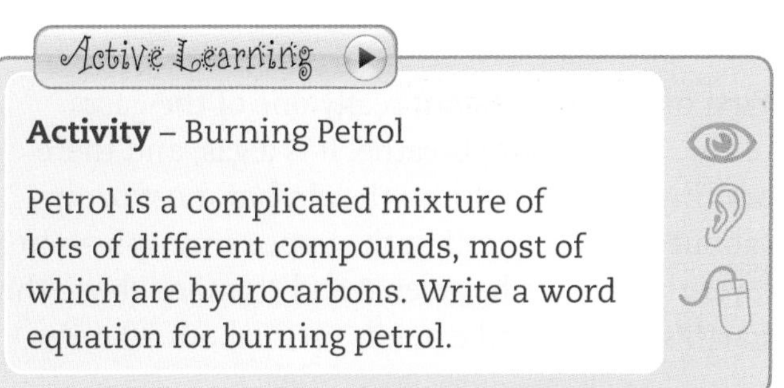

Active Learning

Activity – Burning Petrol

Petrol is a complicated mixture of lots of different compounds, most of which are hydrocarbons. Write a word equation for burning petrol.

Carbon footprint and food miles – responsible citizens?

Your **carbon footprint** is a measure of your impact on the environment and consequently your contribution to climate change. It calculates the quantity of greenhouse gases you produce through burning fossil fuels for electricity, heating and transportation etc. There are many websites which will allow you to calculate yours – try www.direct.gov.uk/actonco2. Food miles compare the distance your food travels from where it is grown, or made, to your plate. A lot of the fruit and vegetables eaten in the UK comes from abroad, despite the fact that much of it could be produced here. A lot of it arrives by plane – and air travel gives off more CO_2 than any other form of transport.

When it arrives here, it is unloaded onto lorries for distribution to supermarkets and shops throughout the country, resulting in further damage to the atmosphere.

Ozone

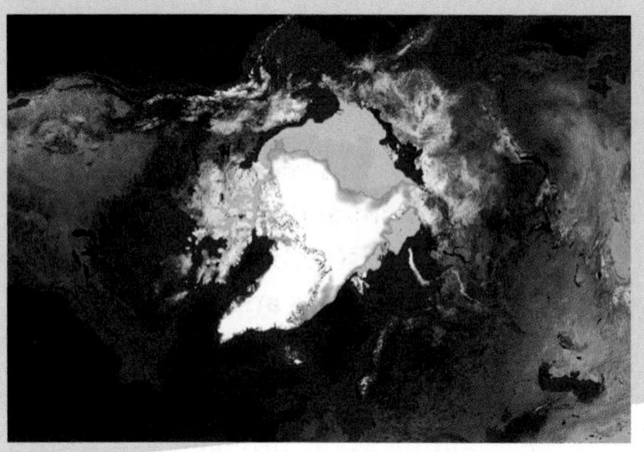

Sea ice is frozen sea water floating on the surface of the ocean. In this image, the white area shows sea ice in the Arctic region in 2007. The blue-green shading shows the area of ice that disappeared between 1979 (when records began) and 2005. The orange shading shows the area of ice that disappeared between 2005 and 2007 – a dramatic reduction in just two years. Has ozone depletion caused this?

Ozone is a gas which has the formula O_3. As you can see it is related to another gas, oxygen, which has the formula O_2. Oxygen molecules contain two atoms of oxygen joined together whereas ozone molecules have three.

First of all, ozone is **not** really one of the gases of the air which we breathe. It is a gas, and there are tiny amounts of it in the air, but most ozone (about 90%) is found in the upper atmosphere in a layer that begins between 6 and 10 miles above the Earth's surface and extends up to about 30 miles.

It is a very useful gas because it **absorbs** some **ultra-violet radiation** coming from the sun and so stops it reaching us on Earth and potentially causing us damage. People often think of the sun as nature's way of giving us daylight and some heat and not much else. The sun does indeed send out light which allows us to see – we call this **visible** light. However, it also sends out **in**visible rays which we cannot see, and some of them can be very harmful. This is ultraviolet or UV radiation. It comes in three types, UVA, UVB and UVC, and it can be very dangerous. Fortunately, the ozone layer above the Earth's atmosphere absorbs much of it, and sunscreens can protect us from what

Ozone

does get through, but damage to the ozone layer means that more and more UV rays are reaching us. Too much exposure to UVB causes sunburn and possibly skin cancer. On the other hand, UVB radiation helps the body produce vitamin D which forms under the skin in reaction to sunlight. Vitamin D is good for producing and maintaining strong, healthy bones and teeth. It also stops us getting SAD! Seasonally Affected Disorder can make otherwise happy people depressed during the winter months due to a lack of sunshine causing a shortage of vitamin D. Fortunately we can also obtain vitamin D from foods such as liver, butter, full-fat milk, oily fish, eggs, margarine, breakfast cereals and powdered milk. So looking after the ozone layer is a good idea – it **protects** us.

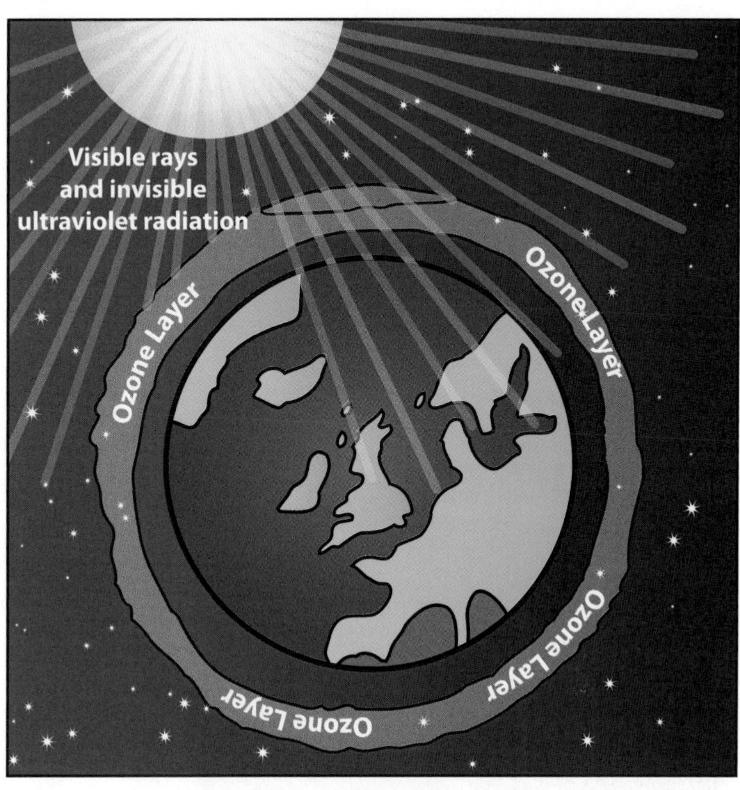

What causes ozone depletion?

Similar to the discovery of global warming, it was towards the end of the twentieth century that scientists identified what became known as 'a hole in the ozone layer', situated above the ice caps at the North Pole. You can probably imagine who had caused this damage… Yes, it was us again! Two very popular consumer items of the twentieth century, fridges and aerosol spray cans, used chemicals called **chlorofluorocarbons**, or **CFCs**, to make them work.

When people disposed of old fridges and empty aerosol cans, they may simply have ended up buried in landfill sites. What was not known until it was too late was that over time the CFCs they contained had leaked out and travelled upwards into the atmosphere. Eventually CFC molecules reacted with ozone molecules and the protective ozone layer began to thin. This is known as **ozone depletion** and it eventually created the hole in the ozone layer. Now that this is known, other so-called ozone friendly chemicals are used instead of CFCs, but the damage has already been done. The harmful ultraviolet radiation which could now reach the Earth can cause severe damage to some plants. As a result, animals which depend on these plants for food would be affected, resulting in the entire **food chain** being upset – and not just on land.

Ozone

Plankton

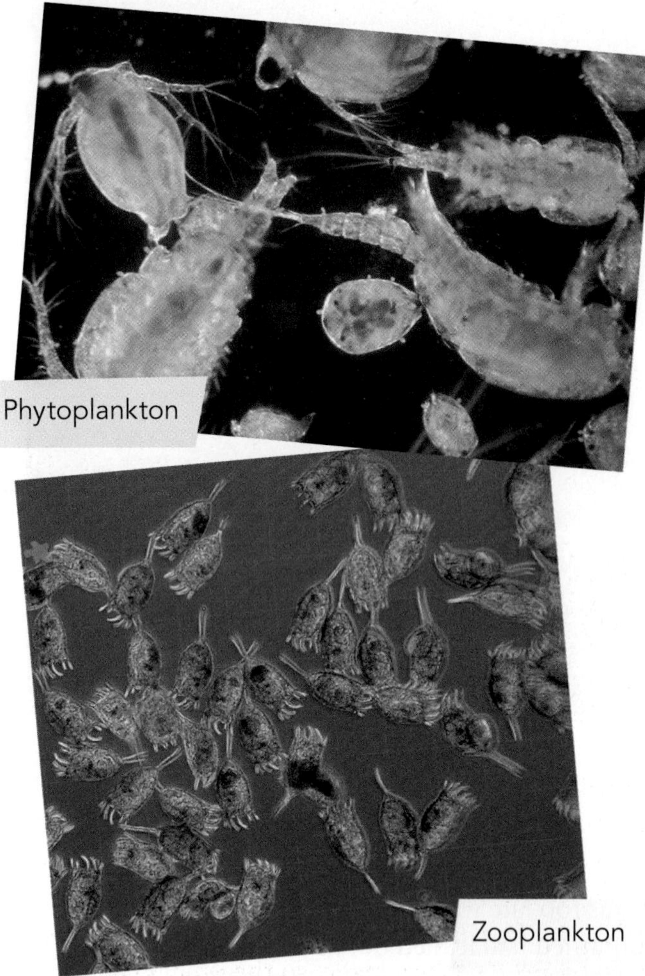

Phytoplankton

Zooplankton

Plankton are tiny animal and vegetable organisms found floating in the oceans and other bodies of water. There are two main types of plankton – phytoplankton and zooplankton. Phytoplankton are basically water plants and so they can photosynthesise. We class them as producers. Zooplankton are animals. They survive by eating different types of plankton. Zooplankton are consumers. Phytoplankton are at the start of all of the food chains and food webs in the oceans. Even some huge mammals such as whales depend on plankton as a food supply.

For example:

Phytoplankton → Krill → Penguins, Seals, Sharks, Sea Birds etc.

For this reason phytoplankton are found near the surface of water – close to the sunlight needed for photosynthesis. The presence of phytoplankton is not just good news for zooplankton or krill which may feed on it, it's good news for us too! During photosynthesis, phytoplankton remove vast quantities of carbon dioxide from the atmosphere. However, in the same way in which UVB radiation can harm us, it is lethal for small organisms such as phytoplankton. The destruction of phytoplankton in this way will not only have a disastrous affect on the ocean's food web, it will result in increased levels of carbon dioxide in the atmosphere leading yet again to global warming.

Active Learning

Activity – What Can We Do To Stop This?

Three simple solutions would be to:

- Stop burning fossil fuels in power stations – find **alternative** ways of making electricity.
- Stop using vehicles which burn petrol and diesel fuel – develop **alternative** forms of transport.
- Dispose of old refrigerators and aerosol cans more carefully and continue to develop CFC-free **alternative** versions.

1 For each solution, will it reduce global warming or ozone depletion? How will this be achieved in each case?

2 Each solution includes the word **alternative**. What does this mean? Try to find out what are the possibilities in each case.

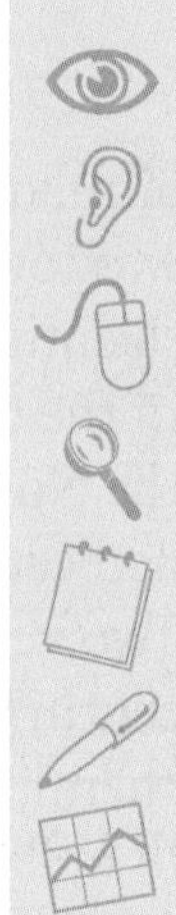

What gear are you in? Carbon neutral!

It seems that an ever increasing demand for electricity combined with a reluctance to give up motor vehicles means that fossil fuels will continue to be burned for the foreseeable future. Remember that this is a global issue – what are other countries doing about it? Let's use up some air miles.

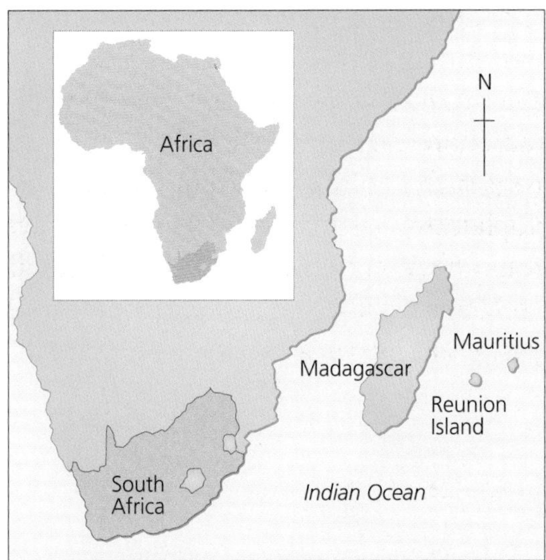

A sugar cane field in Mauritius

The economy of the island of Mauritius in the Indian Ocean depends on tourism, textiles and sugar. The sugar is grown as sugar cane. One of the by-products of the manufacture of sugar is a stringy, fibrous material known as **bagasse**. Years ago this was used as a fuel in sugar factories for generators to provide electricity for use in the factories. Burning bagasse produces carbon dioxide, but this carbon dioxide can be absorbed by growing sugar cane during photosynthesis, so the level of carbon dioxide in the atmosphere does not go up.

The system is said to be **carbon neutral**. Nowadays bagasse is used to produce electricity for the island's people for 6 months of each year during the harvesting season. For the 6 months of planting and growing, Mauritius gets most of its electricity from coal. Let's look more closely at the production of sugar from sugar cane.

Mauritius produces 17 different types of sugar, the most common one being that which we use to sweeten tea and coffee. It is a carbohydrate known as sucrose and it has the chemical formula $C_{12}H_{22}O_{11}$. During its production from sugar cane, many by-products are made, so the process is highly economical. First, the canes are ground up with water in mills to produce a juice – this juice is a solution of sugars in water.

At this stage **filtration** can separate bagasse from the juice ready for burning after drying. Lime (calcium oxide) is added to the juice to clarify it by removing some impurities which make the juice cloudy. This process produces a **scum** which is used to make fertiliser (see Chapter 10). Some water is then evaporated from the clear juice to make the sugar solution more concentrated. The concentrated solution is then spun in a centrifuge to produce sugar crystals and **molasses** – another kind of sugar. Molasses can be used to make rum for drinking or ethanol which can be used as a fuel itself or mixed with petrol to make another fuel known as gasohol.

What gear are you in? Carbon neutral!

Mixing ethanol made from sugar cane with petrol has been done for several years in Brazil. Brazil has no oil wells of its own, and is not a prosperous enough country to be able to import the vast quantities which the population requires. In Mauritius, a flow chart of the processes involved follows:

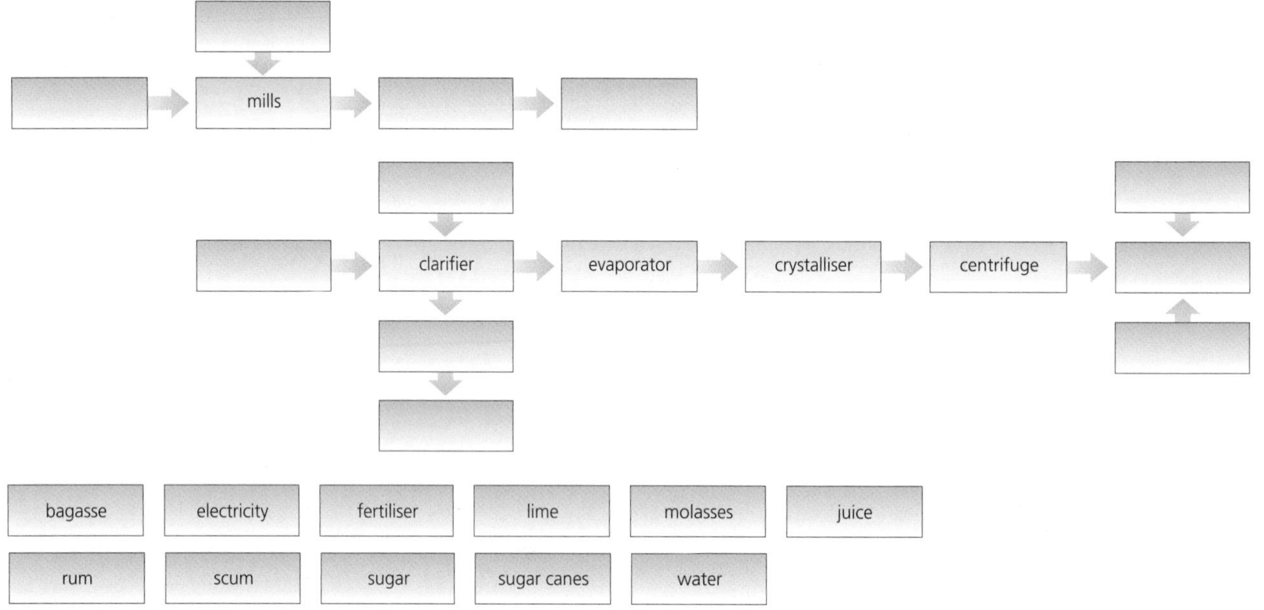

In your jotter, copy and complete the flow chart above by entering the correct word from the given list in each box.

Every little helps

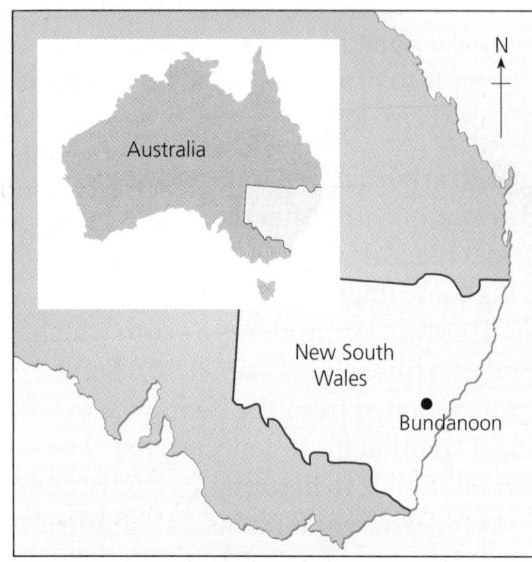

In 2009, the villagers of Bundanoon, in Australia, (population of only around 2000) decided to do away with commercially-produced bottled water. They felt strongly that the production methods of the plastic containers combined with transport and distribution were both contributing too highly to greenhouse gas emissions, and so they decided to try to do without bottled water – many shops and supermarkets agreed not to sell it! So what did they replace it with? The villagers now buy colourful, reusable Bundy-On-Tap plastic bottles, like the ones you may use in the gym, and the village has installed large numbers of chilled water refill points. The water used is the local spring water and although the bottles cost around £2 or so, they will last for a very long time – so the scheme saves people money too!

Closer to home

It's not only in far off countries with lots of sunshine that people can do something about cutting carbon emissions. In the UK small communities and even individuals can make a contribution.

Activities

Research one of the following examples and prepare a presentation for the rest of your class.

1 Find out what the villagers of Ashton Hayes in Cheshire are doing to make their village carbon neutral.

2 Watch the video clip on the zero-carbon house in the Shetland Islands to the north of Scotland. You'll find it at: www.guardian.co.uk/environment/video/2008/may/19/reas.zero.carbon.house.

3 The Americans also have an interesting solution to the problem – making petrol from wood! Ask your teacher to let you watch a video clip on green gasoline (petrol).

4 Scotland has great potential to generate electricity from renewable sources such as inland and offshore wind power and wave power. Find out about current research into these options and prepare a talk to your class which will inform them about where in Scotland and other countries this can be done. There are some people who are against this type of development because of the possible damage to the countryside and seas which they say will result from construction work. Remember to present both sides of the argument in your talk, but do not sit on the fence – which side are **you** on?

Whitelee Wind Farm on Eaglesham Moor is the second largest windfarm in Europe.

Tidal energy systems are being developed which will allow us to generate electricity using the power of the sea.

Some people say that causing the world's population to worry too much about global warming is scare mongering, and that rising carbon dioxide levels do not cause it. These people think that the current noted rise in temperature of the planet is a natural phenomenon which occurs from time to time, and it always results in a rise in carbon dioxide levels in the atmosphere.

Active Learning

1 'What's wrong with global warming? We might lose Holland but there are other places to go on holiday', wrote television celebrity Jeremy Clarkson once in a national newspaper. Famous naturalist David Bellamy also disputes the apparent facts. Find out more about what these two people and others have said about this counter argument and prepare a talk to your class about it.

2 Some companies claim to be carbon neutral. Find out how a company becomes carbon neutral. Do you think this is a genuine claim?

GLOSSARY

Acid rain rain, snow or sleet containing relatively high concentrations of acid-forming chemicals which have been released into the atmosphere and combined with water vapour

Carbon footprint a measure of the amount of carbon dioxide produced by a person, organisation or location at a given time

Carbon neutral not causing increased levels of carbon dioxide in the atmosphere

Chlorofluorocarbon a compound containing the elements chlorine, fluorine and carbon

Filtration a method of separating liquids and undissolved solids

Food chain a series of living things in a community, each of which feeds on another in the chain and is in turn eaten

Global warming an increase in the Earth's average atmospheric temperature that causes corresponding changes in climate

Greenhouse Effect the Earth's natural way of preventing extremes of temperature

Hydrocarbon a compound containing only the elements hydrogen and carbon

Oxide a compound of oxygen and one other element

Ozone a gas found in the stratosphere

Ozone depletion a slow, steady decline in the total volume of ozone in the Earth's **stratosphere**

Photosynthesis a reaction in which green plants make food from carbon dioxide. Oxygen is released

Respiration a reaction in which animals and plants use oxygen to get energy from food. Carbon dioxide is released

Stratosphere a region of the upper atmosphere extending upwards to about 50 km above the Earth

Ultraviolet radiation high energy radiation from beyond the violet end of the visible spectrum

Visible spectrum the range of wavelengths of electromagnetic radiation that is normally visible

Curriculum for Excellence mapping grid

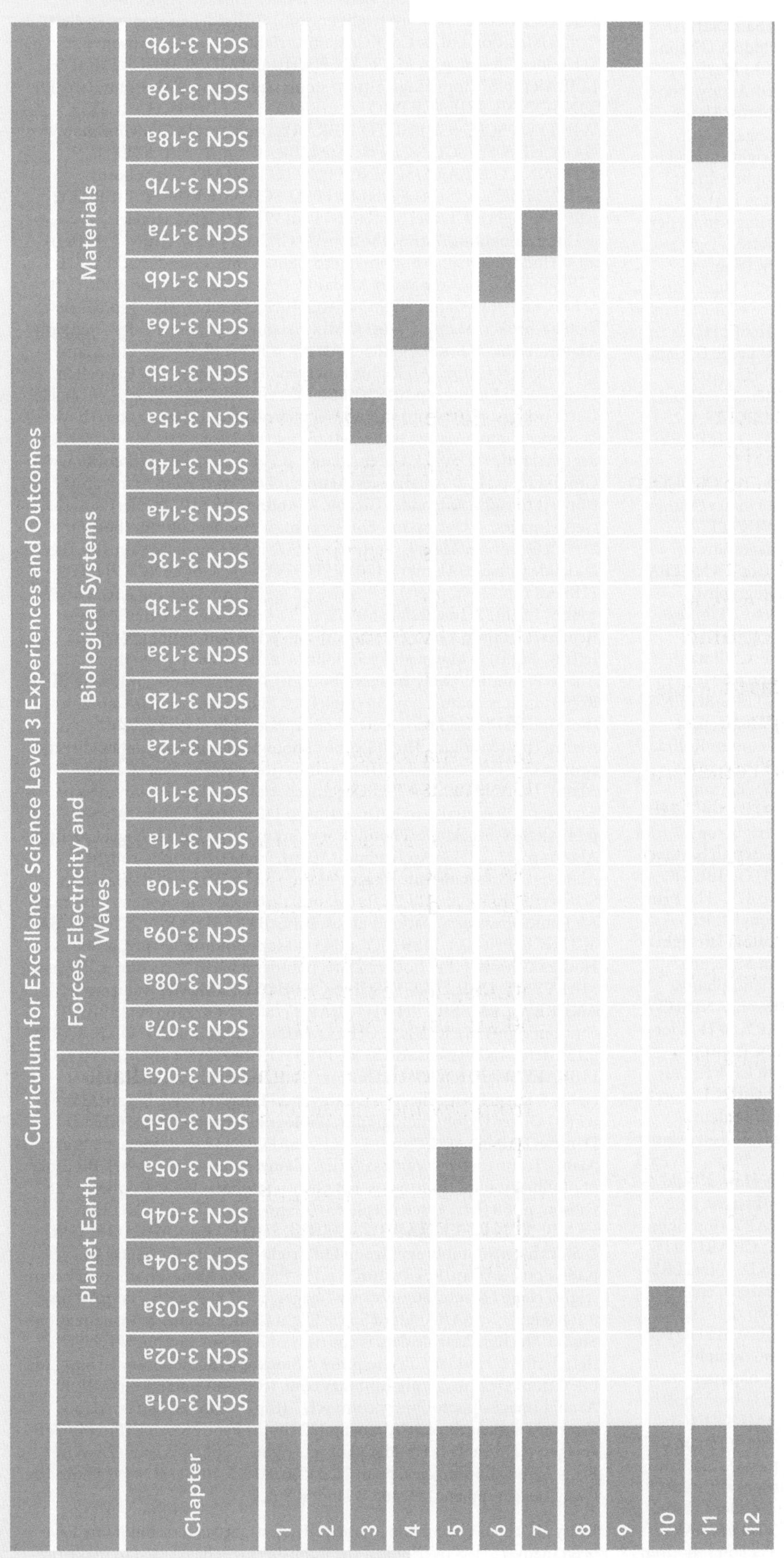

Curriculum for Excellence Science Level 3 Experiences and Outcomes	Planet Earth								Forces, Electricity and Waves						Biological Systems							Materials								
Chapter	SCN 3-01a	SCN 3-02a	SCN 3-03a	SCN 3-04a	SCN 3-04b	SCN 3-05a	SCN 3-05b	SCN 3-06a	SCN 3-07a	SCN 3-08a	SCN 3-09a	SCN 3-10a	SCN 3-11a	SCN 3-11b	SCN 3-12a	SCN 3-12b	SCN 3-13a	SCN 3-13b	SCN 3-13c	SCN 3-14a	SCN 3-14b	SCN 3-15a	SCN 3-15b	SCN 3-16a	SCN 3-16b	SCN 3-17a	SCN 3-17b	SCN 3-18a	SCN 3-19a	SCN 3-19b
1																													■	
2																							■							
3																						■								
4																								■						
5						■																								
6																									■					
7																										■				
8																											■			
9																														■
10			■																											
11																												■		
12							■																							

The Publishers would like to thank the following for permission to reproduce copyright material:

Photo credits

p.7 (left) © Sondra Paulson/iStockphoto.com, (top right) Sami Sarkis/ Photographer's Choice/Getty Images, (bottom right) © Hodder Gibson; p.8 © Mary Evans Picture Library/Alamy; p.9 (top left both) Martyn F. Chillmaid, (bottom left) © mediablitzimages (uk) Limited/Alamy, (top right left) © Hodder Gibson, (top right right) © sciencephotos/Alamy, (bottom right) © Hodder Gibson; p.10 (top) © Phil Degginger/Alamy, (bottom left) © ACE STOCK LIMITED/Alamy, (bottom right) © Hodder Gibson; p.12 (top) Maurice Savage Photography/photographersdirect. com, (bottom) Stockbyte/Stockdisc/Getty Images; p.16 (top left) © Ashley Cooper pics/Alamy, (top right) Clive Streeter/Dorling Kindersley/ Getty Images, (bottom left) © Basement Stock/Alamy, (bottom right) © sciencephotos/Alamy; p.18 (left) © Tetra Images/Alamy, (right) © blickwinkel/Alamy; p.19 © Jacqui Dracup/Alamy; p.22 (left) Nigel Forrow Photography/photographersdirect.com, (right) Nigel Forrow Photography/ photographersdirect.com; p.23 (left) © Trinity Mirror/Mirrorpix/Alamy, (right top left) © sciencephotos/Alamy, (right top right) © Leslie Garland Picture Library/Alamy, (right bottom) © WILDLIFE GmbH/Alamy; p.24 (top both) Maurice Savage Photography/photographersdirect.com, (bottom) CHARLES D. WINTERS/SCIENCE PHOTO LIBRARY; p.25 ANDREW LAMBERT PHOTOGRAPHY/SCIENCE PHOTO LIBRARY; p.27 (top, left to right) ANDREW LAMBERT PHOTOGRAPHY/ SCIENCE PHOTO LIBRARY, CHARLES D. WINTERS/SCIENCE PHOTO LIBRARY, (middle left to right) © Leslie Garland Picture Library/Alamy, © Leslie Garland Picture Library/Alamy, CHARLES D. WINTERS/ SCIENCE PHOTO LIBRARY, (bottom left to right) © ImagesEurope/ Alamy, Martyn F. Chillmaid, Martyn F. Chillmaid; p.28 (top) © MELBA PHOTO AGENCY/Alamy, (bottom) Maurice Savage Photography/ photographersdirect.com; p.29 (left) © Leslie Garland Picture Library/ Alamy, (right) © Phil Degginger/Alamy; p.30 (top left to right) Nigel Forrow Photography/photographersdirect.com, Martyn F. Chillmaid, Martyn F. Chillmaid; (bottom) © Henry Steadman/Alamy; p.31 (top to bottom) © PCN Photography/Alamy, CHARLES D. WINTERS/SCIENCE PHOTO LIBRARY, Warrick Page/Getty Images, © alam/Alamy; p.34 (left) © North Wind Picture Archives/Alamy, (right) © Georgios Kollidas/ Alamy; p.35 RIA NOVOSTI/SCIENCE PHOTO LIBRARY; p.38 (top) RAUL GONZALEZ PEREZ/SCIENCE PHOTO LIBRARY; (bottom) ANDREW LAMBERT PHOTOGRAPHY/SCIENCE PHOTO LIBRARY; p.39 © sciencephotos/Alamy; p.44 (left) © Tim Fletcher; (right top) © Alex Segre/Alamy, (right bottom) © imagebroker/Alamy; p.46 (top to bottom) ANDREW LAMBERT PHOTOGRAPHY/SCIENCE PHOTO LIBRARY, © Hodder Gibson, © Imagestate Media, © Hodder Gibson; p.47 © The Print Collector/Alamy; p.51 (top left) © Fran McDonald, (bottom left left) A © arteretum, www.joannawnuk.com/iStockphoto.com, (bottom left right) Bambu Productions/Iconica/Getty Images, (right) © John McKenna/ Alamy; p.52 (left) © Russell Kord/Alamy, (top right) © sciencephotos/ Alamy, (bottom right, clockwise from top) © Hodder Gibson, ANDREW LAMBERT PHOTOGRAPHY/SCIENCE PHOTO LIBRARY, © Hodder Gibson, © Hodder Gibson; p.53 (left) © Max Nevis/Alamy, (right) © Hodder Gibson; p.55 (top left) © Hodder Gibson, (bottom left left) Guy Ryecart/Dorling Kindersley/Getty Images, (bottom left right) © Decorative Arts/Alamy, (top right) © foodfolio/Alamy, (bottom right) © alam/ Alamy; p.56 © World Pictures/Alamy; p.57 (top) © Joseph Sibilsky/Alamy, (bottom) © Hodder Gibson; p.58 © curved-light/Alamy; p.59 (top) © Paul Rapson/Alamy, (bottom) © Hodder Gibson; p.60 © Chris Howes/Wild Places Photography/Alamy; p.61 © 1992 Photodisc/Getty Images; p.62 (top left) JAMES STEVENSON/SCIENCE PHOTO LIBRARY, (top right) AARON HAUPT/SCIENCE PHOTO LIBRARY, (bottom) CHARLES D. WINTERS/SCIENCE PHOTO LIBRARY; p.63 CHARLES D. WINTERS/ SCIENCE PHOTO LIBRARY; p.67 © NASA Langley Research Center; p.68 (top left) © Jonathan Howell Photography/Alamy, (top right) © Mark Scheuern/Alamy, (bottom) ANDREW SYRED/SCIENCE PHOTO LIBRARY LIBRARY; p.69 (top left both) Nigel Forrow Photography, photographersdirect.com, (bottom left) John Chapman/Chapman Photography/photographersdirect.com, (right) © Hodder Gibson; p.70 (top) © The Trustees of the British Museum, (bottom) JAMES KING-HOLMES/SCIENCE PHOTO LIBRARY; p.71 James Osmond/Britain on View/photolibrary.com; p.73 (left) (left to right from top row) © latham & holmes/Alamy, © felinda - Fotolia.com, © Hodder Gibson, © Hodder Gibson, © Hodder Gibson, © Michael Griffin/Alamy, © Hodder Gibson, © Hodder Gibson, MICHAEL SZOENYI/SCIENCE PHOTO LIBRARY; (top right) Nigel Forrow Photography/photographersdirect.com, (bottom right, left to right) Nigel Forrow Photography/photographersdirect.com, Sapsiwai - fotolia.com, Lisa M. Robinson/Photonica/Getty Images; p.74 © milos luzanin/Alamy; p.78 © Fran McDonald;

p.82 © Hodder Gibson; p.83 (left) © Hodder Gibson, (right) top) © PHOTOTAKE Inc./Alamy, (right bottom) © Hodder Gibson; p. 84 (left) © bilwissedition Ltd. & Co. KG/Alamy, (right) © Hodder Gibson; p.85 © Hodder Gibson; p.86 MARTYN F. CHILLMAID/SCIENCE PHOTO LIBRARY; p.87 (top) Hugh Sitton/Stone/Getty Images, (bottom) GAVIN KINGCOME/SCIENCE PHOTO LIBRARY; p.88 (left) CHARLES D. WINTERS/SCIENCE PHOTO LIBRARY, (right) © Hodder Gibson; p.96 GARY HINCKS/SCIENCE PHOTO LIBRARY; p.97 (left) STEPHEN & DONNA O'MEARA/SCIENCE PHOTO LIBRARY, (right both) SCIENTIFICA, VISUALS UNLIMITED/SCIENCE PHOTO LIBRARY; p.98 (top right) © Travel Scotland – Paul White/Alamy, (top left) © Doug Houghton/Alamy, (bottom) © Graham Uney/Alamy; p.99 (top) all © Hodder Gibson, (bottom left to right) VisitScotland/SCOTTISH VIEWPOINT, © Doug Steley A/Alamy, © Alex Segre/Alamy; p.100 (left) © RF Company/Alamy, (right) © Arco Images GmbH/Alamy; p.101 (left) © imagebroker/Alamy, (right) © Mira/Alamy; p.102 (left) © RF Company/ Alamy, (right) © E.R. Degginger/Alamy; p.103 © BL Images Ltd/Alamy; p.104 (left) © Corbis. All Rights Reserved., (right) Wim van Cappellen/ Lineair/Still Pictures; p.105 ©Dimitri Vervitsiotis/Photographer's Choice/ Getty Images; p.108 (top) © NASA Goddard Space Flight Center, (bottom) © sciencephotos/Alamy; p.109 (left to right) © Imagestate Media, © Alex Segre/Alamy, © David J. Green/Alamy; p.110 © Stockbyte/Photolibrary Group Ltd; p.111 © Albaimages/Alamy; p.116 © Jim West/Alamy; p.117 (top left to right) © Hodder Gibson, © Andrew Ward/Life File/Photodisc/ Getty Images, © Unclesam - Fotolia.com, © Hodder Gibson, (bottom left) © Alex Genovese/Alamy, (bottom right) © John Sturrock/Alamy; p.119 © claude thibault/Alamy; p.120 GIPHOTOSTOCK/SCIENCE PHOTO LIBRARY; p.121 (top left) © Positive image/Alamy, (bottom left) © ICP/ Alamy, (right) © Imagestate Media; p.124 © PAT COCCIADIFERRO/ Reuters/Corbis; p.125 © Hodder Gibson; p.126 (left, both) © Stephen Jeffrey, (right) © Marmaduke St. John/Alamy; p.128 (top) Arthur S. Aubry/Photodisc/Getty Images, (bottom) © Redfx/Alamy; p.129 Geoffrey Robinson/Rex Features; p.130 (topleft) © PhotoStock-Israel/Alamy, (bottom left) © Michael T Jones/Alamy, (top right) © imagebroker/ Alamy, (bottom right) Hugh Penney Photography, photographersdirect. com; p.135 (left) © Nigel Cattlin/Alamy, (top right) © Nigel Cattlin/ Alamy, (bottom right) © Phil Degginger/Alamy; p.136 © Libby Welch/ Alamy; p.138 © gualtiero boffi/Alamy; p.140 © Nigel Cattlin/Alamy; p.141 (left) © Stockbyte/Photolibrary Group Ltd, (right) © Nigel Cattlin/ Alamy; p.142 (left) © Arcticphoto/Alamy, (right) © Derek Croucher/ Alamy; p.143 © economic images/Alamy; p.144(left to right) Hartmut Schwarzbach/argus/Still Pictures/Specialiststock.com, Ronen Zilberman/ AP Photo/Press Association Photos, BILL BARKSDALE/AGSTOCKUSA/ SCIENCE PHOTO LIBRARY; p.145 © Mark Boulton/Alamy; p.146 © Hodder Gibson; p.149 Robert Clare, photographersdirect.com; p.150 (top) MARTYN F. CHILLMAID/SCIENCE PHOTO LIBRARY, (bottom left) ANDREW LAMBERT PHOTOGRAPHY/SCIENCE PHOTO LIBRARY, (bottom right) MARTYN F. CHILLMAID/SCIENCE PHOTO LIBRARY; p.151 (left) ANDREW LAMBERT PHOTOGRAPHY/SCIENCE PHOTO LIBRARY, (right top left and bottom) © Hodder Gibson, (right top right) © idp garden collection/Alamy; p.154 (left) © Dave Bevan/Alamy, (right) Oliver Dixon Photography, photographersdirect.com; p.156 © DanieleC/Alamy; p.157 (top) © ALIKI SAPOUNTZI/aliki image library/ Alamy, (centre left) © Vanessa Miles/Alamy, (centre right) Mark Boulton/ photolibrary.com, (bottom) © Jan Quist - fotolia; p.158 © Hodder Gibson; p.160 (left) © sciencephotos/Alamy, (right, both) ANDREW LAMBERT PHOTOGRAPHY/SCIENCE PHOTO LIBRARY; p.161 (left) © Stockbyte/Photolibrary Group Ltd, (right) © Photodisc/Getty Images; p.164 Francis Dean/Rex Features; p.165 (left) Stockbyte/Photolibrary.com, (right) Nello Giambi/Stone/Getty Images; p.167 © Peter Bowater/Alamy; p.168 (right) NASA/Goddard Space Flight Center Scientific Visualization Studio The Blue Marble data is courtesy of Reto Stockli (NASA/GSFC), (left, both) © Hodder Gibson; p.169 © Stockbyte/Photolibrary Group Ltd; p.170 (top) Dex Image/photolibrary.com, (bottom) Roland Birke/Peter Arnold Images/photolibrary.com; p.171 (top) © Fabrice Bettex/Alamy, (bottom) © imagebroker/Alamy; p.172 (both) Penny SPANKIE/AFP/Getty Images; p.173 (left) © Hodder Gibson, (right) Stephen Wilson/PA Wire/ Press Association Images. pp.6, 21, 33, 50, 80, 93, 107, 123, 148 © Photodisc/ Getty Images. pp.66, 133, 163 © Digital Stock.

Every effort has been made to trace all copyright holders, but if any have been inadvertently overlooked the Publishers will be pleased to make the necessary arrangements at the first opportunity.